# *Still Standing After All the Tears*

# WORKBOOK

## *Faith In the Battle Edition*

## Valerie Silveira and Dawn R. Ward

# STILL STANDING AFTER ALL THE TEARS WORKBOOK

## Faith In the Battle Edition

Published by: The Still Standing Group

ISBN: 978-0-9861104-6-7

Cover Illustration by: Svetlana Dragicevic

## Companion Workbook to:

# Still STANDING

## AFTER ALL THE TEARS

STRENGTH  MEANING  SELF-LOVE
FAITH  DECIDE  ATTITUDE
CONTROL  STAND UP  FOCUS

## PUTTING BACK THE PIECES AFTER
## ALL HELL BREAKS LOOSE

### NINE ACTIONS TO BATTLE YOUR BEAST

Valerie Silveira

# What People Are Saying

We recommend "Still Standing After All the Tears" and use the companion Workbook in our addiction ministry at two separate churches. Out of all the materials we have used in our eleven-year history, yours are by far the best. Everyone I give the books to say they can't put them down. Valerie, I am so glad God brought me to your ministry; it has also been a Godsend for me. I am so excited for the Faith in the Battle Workbook edition. Thank you!
**~Sandra Schuk, Founder, Thread of Hope Addiction Ministry**

"I am grateful and encouraged that Dawn has poured out her wisdom into this workbook! She has found the best path to love others in a way that promotes healing and purpose. I believe her journey and life victories will reflect in the content of these Nine Actions tools. She has moved from enabling loved ones to restoring them. Be encouraged"
**~ Cesar Sanchez MSW, LADC, Christian Counselor and Clinical Director**

"I so admire Valerie for her courage, tenacity and fire within to get her message out to us parents. She peels away at the shame we carry with us and shows us how to be happy and joyful, even if our children are struggling. Valerie is a walking and breathing example of her message and makes a huge contribution to the world out of the pain she has experienced with her daughter."
**~Kate Rogers**

"Every once in a while, a person will come into your life at the exact moment you need them. Dawn has a way with words that strikes at your very soul, both shattering lies from the enemy and applying a healing balm at the same time! Putting God's word above her own, she is able to remind you that that addiction does not own you, and Jesus has already won the battle."
**~ Donna Speakman**

"I have joined/followed/liked/attended/read/re-read/researched many meetings, articles, studies, books, FB pages, and support groups. I want you to know I have gotten more understanding, empathy, sympathy, support, and encouragement from your books, posts, and emails than any of the above. Your story somehow connects with me on a gut and heart level, and leaves me feeling stronger and more hopeful & peaceful than any of the above."
**— Robin Singleton**

"Dawn and I were complete strangers until we meet on a site for moms of addicts. We began our friendship we prayed daily and we read Valerie Silveira's book, Still Standing After All the Tears and we began to use the Nine Actions to Battle Your Beast. As we prayed daily the Lord was using his word and our prayers to set us free. Our faith grew and our lives showed our new-found faith and love for our children, ourselves and most importantly our love for Jesus! He showed us that all things are possible for those who love him!"
**~Patty Wildman**

# *Foreword*

The book you hold in your hands is the work of two precious women/mothers who each endured the sadness of learning their children had become addicted to life-altering substances. The difficulty of ministering to drug-addicted children is one where the helper can, unwittingly, become a second casualty of the problem. Valerie and Dawn learned "the hard way" that the kingdom of darkness which seeks to destroy the life of the addict will attempt to maximize destructive results through collateral damage. Valerie and Dawn have prayerfully and carefully organized this material with the intent of providing tools for families to effectively navigate the storm-tossed chaos of drug addiction while not becoming a casualty of it.

As a Pastor since 2000, living in "Sin City," I asked the Lord long ago if I should get out of this town. I received the reply that I was called to stay in order to assist others as they pick up the pieces of their broken lives after "taking the bait" of the kingdom of darkness. I carefully align myself with people who recognize the need to be "salt and light" in a city of diabolically crafted facades. I am thrilled to recommend the work of Valerie and Dawn who I consider to be fellow warriors and partners in the work of saving lives of lost and broken people. May God bless their efforts as they embrace such important work.

Mike Welte
Pastor, Calvary Chapel Meadow Mesa
North Las Vegas, NV

# *The Authors' Collaboration*

**Valerie Silveira** published "Still Standing After All the Tears," and the companion "Still Standing After All the Tears Workbook" in 2015. These books are helping thousands of women to stand up and battle their Beasts, and to reclaim their lives.

**Dawn R. Ward** has been a student of Valerie's work starting just months after she published the referenced books. In this version of the Still Standing After All the Tears Workbook, we wanted to speak directly into the lives of the Christian community to help them grow stronger spiritually while standing up and battling their Beasts.

Unless noted, all sections of the book, other than the Faith in the Battle sections, were authored by Valerie. The Faith In the Battle Sections were written by Dawn.

The Declarations have been updated for this version of the Workbook, as well as other minor changes from Valerie's work in the original Workbook.

# Authors' Disclaimers

This publication is not intended as a substitute for the advice of a health care professional.

The authors' personal stories have been told to the best of their recollection. Certain conversations and events were combined or condensed in order to stay on point. The names of most of the individuals have been changed, including Valerie's daughter, whom she chose to call "Jordan," in her first three books, including the original Workbook. Since the publishing of Valerie's first three books, her daughter was killed. Since her death, Valerie now tells readers "Jordan's" name was Jamie. In order to avoid confusion, she has decided to continue to call her daughter Jordan in subsequent versions of the Workbook.

Credit has been given to the author of quotes to the best of our ability. Many quotes are attributed to multiple sources, revised, or repeated so many times the original source of the quote may not be known.

We tend to use metaphors in everyday speech and storytelling and have found that they are incredibly relatable for this subject matter. Therefore, we have chosen to use a few of them in our written works.

Valerie references her inability to save her daughter from herself and that we cannot save other people. In these instances, she is referring to adults who understand their actions and choices.

We apologize in advance for our lack of perfect grammar, or if our writing styles wouldn't earn us an "A" in English class. It's more important to us that we connect with people who need help than to write perfectly.

We do not pretend to be bible scholars. In the Faith in the Battle sections, scriptures are referenced with the purpose of supporting the Nine Actions. We made our best effort to reference scriptures within their proper context, realizing that there is a margin for personal interpretation. We have done so with the intention that "All Scripture is God-breathed and is useful for teaching, rebuking, correcting and training in righteousness, so that the servant of God may be thoroughly equipped for every good work." 2 Timothy 3:16-17NIV

# *Valerie's Acknowledgements*

I am forever grateful to my husband, Rich Silveira, who has never wavered in his love for me, or his belief in me and my mission.

To my son, Sean Maher, my sunshine. We have been through a great deal in our lives together, and I am thankful each and every day for your strength, wisdom and courage.

A special thank you to my co-author and friend, Dawn R. Ward. I am eternally grateful that God caused our paths to cross, and that you heard the call to join forces with me. Your love and support go far beyond our work together, and I will never forget how you showed up when it mattered most. I love you, sister.

My thanks to Kalen Arreola for stepping up to help move this book along, and for always knowing what to say and how to say it, in so few words. You are loved and appreciated.

My love and gratitude go to my friend, Annelle Abernethy, for helping me behind the scenes, and for believing in my work enough to stand up and lead groups of women in the battle with their Beasts. You are a treasure.

I am humbled and encouraged by the outpouring of support for the companion book to this Workbook, *Still Standing After All the Tears: Putting Back the Pieces After All Hell Breaks Loose.* Knowing that I am making even a small difference in your life, is what gets me up each morning, with a grateful heart.

Everything I am that is good is by the grace of God. If not for spiritual guidance and the hope of heaven, none of this would be possible, because I would still be down on the mat with my Beast on top of me. Knowing Jamie is safely in the arms of Jesus gives me the courage to keep going.

A heart full of thanks goes out to those of you who have bravely shared your stories with me and trusted me to guide you in your journey to become women of courage. We are in this together, and it is my honor to stand with you.

# *Dawn's Acknowledgements*

I am grateful beyond words for my family and friends that supported me on this path. Each of you believed in me while I was still down on the mat with my Beast's choke-hold around my throat.

For my family, thank you for loving me through this journey and not giving up on me. For my husband, Steve, you have always been such a stabilizing presence in my life and are my biggest cheerleader. For my sons, you have fought your battles with your Beasts with strength and courage. I have learned so much and grown as a person being your mom. For my daughter, Jadyn, you are my hero and the best daughter I could ever hope for.

For the women I have met on this journey, and for my fellow administrators in our Christian Moms of Addicts Facebook group, your faith inspires me. Thank you for your service to our hurting moms and for supporting me in this vision.

Thank you, Valerie Silveira, for believing in me and inviting me to participate in this project with you. You are a woman of true-grit, quick-wittedness, and genuine compassion. I am humbled by your faith in me and honored to call you my friend.

I stand in awe of my amazing Lord and Savior, Jesus Christ, who has directed my feet every step of the way. Thank you for holding me close and keeping a tight grip on my hand. I can only imagine where I would be without you.

# *What is a Beast?*

**Valerie**

*Beasts* come in all shapes and sizes. Some arrive as a result of an alcoholic or addict in the family, abuse, abandonment, an accident or illness, loss, perfectionism, or something else. Many are a combination of two or more. A Beast is that situation, person, attitude, or circumstance that has left you lost, defeated, frustrated, angry, hopeless and helpless, or living in paralyzing fear. Our Beasts remind us of the past, keep us from living in the present, and fearful of the future.

God is the source of all that is good, and Satan is the opposite. If there is a school of Beasts, Satan is the headmaster. I call him the Big Beast.

**Dawn**

All Beasts are a direct result of the Big Beast – Satan, who tries to destroy us personally, as well as our faith. These Beasts set themselves up against the work of God in our lives in an attempt to control us and keep us from living the abundant life God has called us to.

*"Put on the full armor of God, so that you can take your stand against the devil's schemes." Ephesians 6:11*

# Valerie's Introduction

In August 2004, my only daughter suffered a near-fatal gunshot wound, at the hands of her ex-boyfriend, a gang member.

Three years prior to the shooting, Jordan made her way from our safe, comfortable suburban life, into another world. We spent those three years leading up to the shooting, attempting to get her off her collision course. In the hospital after the shooting, I stayed by Jordan's side nearly twenty-four hours a day. Laying in the dark one night in my makeshift bed pressed up against her hospital bed, my eighteen-year-old daughter asked, "Mommy, will you pray with me?"

She had never asked me to pray before, and frankly, I'm not very comfortable praying out loud, but that night I held her hand and prayed my heart out. Afterward, it felt as if our nightmare would end, but it was far from over. I would need to put on my seatbelt and strap down my shoulder harness. My ride on the Roller Coaster From Hell was about to get a lot worse.

It would take a few years into the ride to confirm what I had suspected; Jordan was a drug addict and was eventually addicted to heroin.

As any parent would, I tried everything I knew in an attempt to save Jordan from her drug addiction Beast. I put on my Supermom Cape and came to her rescue time and time again. My help never moved Jordan closer to battling her Beast, but I couldn't stop trying to save her. The further her life spiraled downward; the further mine spiraled into darkness.

My Beast was a two-headed monster. Not only was I an enabler, but my happiness and sense of purpose had become dependent upon my daughter's willingness to battle her Beast. I was codependent.

The best way I know how to describe nearly thirteen years of my life is that I was shoved, kicking and screaming onto a roller coaster with my Codependent Enabler Beast by my side. I rode it painfully up one hill and screaming down the next, trapped in a cycle of a

1

mother's hope and suffocating disappointment. With every twist and turn, fear gripped me, and I held on for dear life.

The ride took me through health issues, a web of lies, financial stress, and a broken family. I rode through a world I never wanted to know, the legal system, failed rehabs for Jordan, a serious strain on my marriage, and constant emotional pain.

No matter what the consequences were for my health, finances, or marriage, I continued to strap on the Supermom Cape, choosing to believe the lies and accept the deceit. I covered my ears and eyes and tried to convince myself "this time it was different." At the core of my actions were love and fear. I desperately wanted my baby back, and I was terrified of what might happen if I pulled out the safety net; if I took off the Supermom Cape.

It seemed everybody else's kids were doing well while I was living every parent's worst nightmare - losing a child, over and over again. My heart was shattered into a million pieces, standing helplessly as my precious daughter lost herself to drug addiction, despite how much I tried to help her. There was no closure and no way to heal. I was stuck. The world was turning without me, without Jordan, without us. With each failed attempt at saving her, I convinced myself I was a colossal failure as a parent; the part of me I valued most.

One day I asked myself the same question I had asked Jordan many times, "Where is your rock bottom?"

It was then that I realized a simple truth - if I had the ability to save Jordan from herself, from her Beast, I would have done it long ago. I had hit my rock bottom.

The Supermom Cape did not detach without pain, but I removed it; I stopped enabling Jordan. The codependency part of my Beast didn't go down as easily. My heart ached for my daughter whose twenties were slipping into the past while she was lost in the belly of her Beast. I missed Jordan every second of every day.

Eventually, I began to accept that my best days were behind me. I was a victim who had been unfairly handed a "life sentence." I was at my lowest point, about to give up, when I made a decision that quite possibly saved my life. I decided to Stand Up and Battle My

2

Beast. I share my very painful and personal journey that shattered my heart into a million pieces, and the actions I took to put those pieces back together.

Since I am the mother of a drug addict, some of what you read will be from that perspective. If you are a mother of an addict, this book is for you. If you have a family member or loved one who is an addict, this book is for you. If you are an addict, this book may be for you - it will help you to understand why it seems at times, that your loved one is crazy.

If your Beast has nothing to do with addiction, this book is still for you. No matter what Beast you have been living with, the Nine Actions to Battle Your Beast could mean the difference between living and really living.

## <u>*Update to Valerie's Story*</u>

On the morning of August 29, 2016, I got that knock on the door; the knock all moms of addicts fear.

I had done the work in this book, so my Beast was very much under control. He would occasionally knock on my door, but I had learned not to answer it. That morning, he didn't knock; he broke my door down – a home invasion.

A beautiful young woman around my daughter's age delivered the news - Jamie died the night before. Detectives arrived the next day to let us know she died from multiple gunshot wounds to the chest. Yes, that dropped me to my knees. I rolled over onto my back, and my Beast got on top of me, in that comfortable place where he had been for so many years. This time I only stayed down for a short while. Although my heart was once again shattered, I am a much stronger and courageous woman. I have the peace that surpasses all understanding. It wasn't long before I decided to once again Stand Up and Fight. That is just what I have done.

## *Dawn's Introduction*

"Our son is using drugs ..." The words my husband spoke hit me like a tsunami. The bottom fell out (more like was "yanked out") from under me. I was no longer standing on solid ground; actually, I had no footing at all. The waters were rising quickly, and if we even survived this, things would never be the same for any of us. Determined to save my son and to save my family, I went into fight mode and got to work. Little did I know how deep these waters were and how unprepared I was to face the enemy's repeated barrage of assaults against my son, my family, and my faith.

We were the classic "all-American" family. We loved our children, supported their education, put them in sports, and took them to church. So, how was this happening to us? Matthew was smart, athletic, and talented. He had everything he needed to succeed in life, and I believed he was destined (and still is) for greatness. He was in his senior year of high school, so why was he "determined" to throw it all away? Why did he start using in the first place? The story of his journey to this day remains quite personal, and he keeps most of it private. I will never know the confusion, hopelessness, and despair he must have felt during that time; but I do know the flood of emotions that swept over me took my breath away as I lunged face-first into this world I had no desire to visit. Deep waters had engulfed me, and I could barely breathe or even pray for that matter. But, cry out I did to a faithful God who promised to never leave me or abandon me. I held onto Him for dear life as I entered this journey of uncertainty and the unknown.

*"If the Lord had not been on our side-the flood would have engulfed us, the torrent would have swept over us, the raging waters would have swept us away."* **Psalm 124:1,4**

The statistics I read informed me the likelihood this disease could be beat was very slim. Questions came much faster than the answers; answers contradicted each other, as did the multitude of experts we consulted. A young boy became a man the day he turned eighteen

5

and checked himself into rehab. As we drove away, we prayed and crossed our fingers and tried to convince ourselves and each other that we caught this early enough; he would spend a few weeks getting the help he needed, and then we could all go back to our normal lives. If only it were that easy.

Fast forward a few years later after our lives had taken every turn imaginable, and it felt as though the dust might finally settle. Our son had received treatment, but more importantly, the Lord had done an amazing work in his life, and he was finally in a good place. Yet, once again, addiction crouched at our front door ready to claim its next victim, and that it did. This time it would be our oldest son, Kyle, who would be unable to escape its grip. It was then we learned how easy it is for someone to become dependent upon prescription pain medications given to them following surgery. The medical professionals we had trusted knew little about the harm they were causing as they wrote prescriptions to treat his chronic pain. They also brought welcomed relief from the constant anxiety that had haunted him since his teenage years. Kyle had everything going for him. He was in his final year of college and looking forward to an exciting career upon graduation. He was gifted artistically and blessed with an incredible sense of humor. Sadly, addiction doesn't play favorites, and another tsunami with its fierce undertow was preparing to pull us back into all-too familiar, unwanted waters.

*"I sink in the miry depths, where there is no foothold. I have come into the deep waters; the floods engulf me. **Psalm 69:2***

Prayers are not always answered quickly. The manuscript of Kyle's life is a work in progress as he continues to struggle with the reality that his Beast has stolen so much from him. The judgment he once passed onto his younger brother now stares back at him reminding him that he is "no better." In fact, in his own eyes, he is far worse. His struggle has tarried longer and cost him inarguably more. His journey has been one of extreme highs and lows. Releasing my adult son into the clutches of the enemy's grip and trusting that our Lord would not let that grip hold too tightly or for too long has not been any easier because I went through it once before. In fact, it was the complete opposite. Instead of my faith becoming stronger, I accepted this trial less and resisted it more. The wounds that I believed had started to heal resurfaced and were a deep and constant reminder that my faith was weak. I was weak. I skillfully hid my pain from most of my family and friends, yet isolation had its price. With false promises of safety, I was called back into the shadows of guilt and shame, and willingly I followed. Christ offered me gifts of grace, comfort, and mercy, but they were rejected as I deemed myself unworthy to receive them. In spite of the lies I believed, a small seed of hope managed to stay alive in the middle of the ash heap, so I held on to that little seed for dear life.

I wish I could say that these transforming lessons I learned were done so with grace and elegance. This was not the case, and my husband will be more than happy to vouch for that. What I can say is that I finally had that "Aha" moment when I took a good, honest look at my life and decided that it had become no life at all. I needed to decide if I truly trusted Jesus with the life of my son because if I didn't, I had to stop pretending that I did. I had to stop trying to control everything and let him go. I decided as a step of faith that I was willing to risk rejection and judgment if telling my story might open the door to my healing and perhaps help another hurting mom. It meant I did not have to have all the answers and know the end of our story before I believed that the Lord could make beauty out of ashes. It is my desire to share that hope with you. I pray you will be able to release your situation or loved one into the safe arms of Jesus, letting go and letting Him faithfully strengthen you, heal you, and grow you into all He desires you to be.

*"In his kindness God called you to share in his eternal glory by means of Christ Jesus. So, after you have suffered a little while, he will restore, support, and strengthen you, and he will place you on a firm foundation."*
**1 Peter 5:10 New Living Translation**

I remember how I first came to learn about Valerie's books and materials. Anyone who knows me knows I like bargains. I didn't like spending a lot of money on books not knowing if they would help, so I googled anything I could find on search engines such as "moms of addicted children, Christian moms of addicts, and help for moms of addicts." I came upon Valerie's web page and signed up for her emails. I took advantage of all her free advice and goodies. I appreciated her openness and candidness regarding her personal experience with fighting her own Beast. Valerie decided to share her story before she knew the last page of the last chapter. What appealed to me more than anything was that she "got me." She seemed to know I was over being obsessed with fixing my addicted child and would have stopped a long time ago if I knew how. Then to my pleasant surprise, she offered a $1 special on her book, Still Standing After All The Tears on Amazon. It's not that I am really all that cheap, but in the world of addiction and recovery, while there is great information out to help the addicts in their recovery, there is little to help the families, especially the moms. Based on what I had already learned through her emails, I felt safe spending my hard-earned dollar. Coincidentally, the book did not download to my Kindle, and I emailed customer service to request help. Somehow in the process, Valerie reached out to me to make sure I got my book and, in her amazing Valerie way, began to remind me that I was worth fighting for and that I had a story to stand on. I connected with her because I knew beyond a shadow of a doubt that she had read my mind prior to writing her book. She encouraged me to purchase the workbook and work the Nine Actions. Over the next few months we corresponded back and forth a few times, and I shared with her how I used her workbook coupled with scriptures to take it even deeper. The idea for this Christian workbook was birthed in both of our hearts (although she had been thinking about it for a long time). In the process, we became kindred spirits. I never saw myself writing a book at all, and am deeply humbled that Valerie felt safe to bring me along on her journey.

# *How to Use the Workbook*

This Workbook is a companion to the book, **"Still Standing After All the Tears: Putting Back the Pieces After All Hell Breaks Loose."** This version of the Workbook was co-authored by Dawn R. Ward. All Faith in the Battle Sections were authored by Dawn.

We recommend that you first read that book and then move on to this Workbook. In an effort to include as much valuable study material, much of Valerie's personal story and some insights from the book have been removed from the Workbook.

Take as much time as you need to work through each of the Nine Actions to Battle Your Beast, but stay consistent. The more Actions you get working at the same time, the more synergy you will create, which in turn will allow you to gain momentum. Do not get stuck too long on one Action, as you can always go through the Actions again.

Make the decision to fight for as long as it takes, no matter what, until you are standing over the top of your Beast. It is crucial that, eventually, you work all Nine Actions simultaneously. Each one supports and works synergistically with the others.

Tips:

- Choose a few minutes of uninterrupted time for study.
- Schedule your study time, making it a priority. You are worth it.
- Eliminate distractions: turn off your cell phone, and resist the urge to check your email.
- Let your family or others in the home know that this time is important and that you are committed to putting the pieces back together.
- Have a pen or pencil handy.
- Use your bible or a bible app for each study. When looking up scriptures, look up as many or as few as time permits, but don't skip this important part of the study.
- Although there is room to write in designated spaces and in the page margins, have some paper available to write extra notes or to journal your thoughts.

You are not required to share your study with anyone, so feel free to be honest. However, if you have a close friend or group of friends, you may choose to get together and go over each section of the Workbook together. People in your Inner Circle can provide perspective and insight that you may not gain by working solely on your own.

 **For all of the original sections of the Workbook, each question or work section for you to journal or answer a question is preceded by a heart bullet and is bolded, as this sentence is.**

 **In the Faith in the Battle sections, each question or area for you to journal is preceded by a dove.**

Space has been provided after bullets for you to write your answers and thoughts, as well as additional room in the margins. Feel free to start a journal or notebook if you need extra room.

All scriptures referenced are the NIV version unless noted.

Valerie & Dawn

# *My Beast*

## My Codependent Enabler Beast

My Beast was a two-headed monster. Not only was I an enabler, but my happiness and sense of purpose had become dependent upon my daughter's willingness to battle her Beast. I was codependent. This was my Beast.

One definition of codependency is: "A codependent person is one who has let another person's behavior affect him or her, and who is obsessed with controlling that person's behavior."

An enabler is defined as "One who enables another to achieve an end; especially: one who enables another to persist in self-destructive behavior (a substance abuse) by providing excuses or making it possible to avoid the consequences of such behavior."

Around and around I went, tortured by what was happening to my daughter, powerless to stop it, and unwilling to move on with my life until it did stop. Clearly, I was living with a Beast.

## Supermom to the Rescue

I am convinced that mothers are given an invisible cape to take home with their newborn babies. We use it every time our child needs rescuing, sometimes long after they reach adulthood.

You expect to use the Supermom Cape when your son falls and skins his knee, or when a boy breaks your daughter's heart. It seems perfectly acceptable to use the Cape when your child pulls a high school prank. Never could you imagine your Cape will be used in an attempt to save your children from themselves.

In the years after the shooting, Jordan continued all of the same behavior she had prior to the shooting and worse. She spent her twenties going from job to job or no job at all. I spent most of her twenties with my Cape on, coming to her rescue. I paid security deposits, rents, car loans, insurance payments, traffic tickets, fines, and medical bills. I bought groceries, clothing, supplements, household items, toiletries, and even perfume! Each time she abandoned her belongings, I bought her more.

I took her to have her ankle bracelet put on and stayed close to her while she wore it for 30 days. I paid for bail bonds and sent money to jails for incidentals and telephone calls. I hired an attorney, paid for drug treatments and drove thousands of miles to retrieve her when she was extradited to another state. And the list goes on.

The point is that I spent tens of thousands of dollars, cried gazillions of tears, and allowed my heart to be shattered into a million pieces, but none of that helped. Jordan and her Beast lied to me and deceived me so many times that I wasn't sure which end was up. Jordan is my daughter, and I didn't know how to stop, so I kept going back for more.

I cried, begged, pleaded, yelled and screamed, threatened to cut her off, and changed my phone number. I swore I would not spend another dime, and then found myself opening up my wallet, one more time.

I had a Supermom Cape, and I wasn't afraid to use it. My husband wanted to rip the Cape off me a hundred times, so I did my best to hide it from him. The woman who stood for integrity was betraying her husband's trust by helping Jordan behind his back. I hated myself for doing it but convinced myself that I was only protecting him.

Years later, I was heartbroken and worn out, Jordan had not been saved, and I was standing before my husband asking for forgiveness.

## Shame, Guilt, and Stigma

### Shame

In anticipation of Jordan choosing rehab, I made some phone calls. One was a well-known local facility. Most rehabs have sliding scales, so I inquired as to a rate for their program for someone without financial means and was told it was $10,000. Unfortunately, Jordan didn't have $10. She explained that an option would be another recovery center in a nearby town. Their financial assistance program would be $5,000. She was very complimentary toward the other treatment center and stated that many of their counselors had gone through that very treatment program.

I knew the area where the center was, right smack in the middle of the drug area of that town. I voiced my concern, letting her know I did not want Jordan around "those kinds of people."

She replied, "Your daughter is taking street drugs. She is one of those people."

I nearly fell off my chair. She was right, but it was painful to hear. By this time, Jordan had admitted to an addiction to opiates. I was certain she was using heroin since there was no way she could afford pills. Still, that word was hard to hear.

It wasn't easy to connect the dots between the incredibly gifted Jordan, and the Jordan who was now being described as "one of those people." Not only would I need to accept the fact that my daughter was a heroin addict, but to face the reality that I was the mother of a heroin addict. The shame that I already felt multiplied.

To say I had high hopes for Jordan's life from the time she was a toddler is putting it mildly. Jordan is very intelligent, athletic, artistic, and witty. We measure our parenting success or failure, to a certain degree, based on where our children are in their lives. Our self-worth is tied to our children, and when they make wrong choices, our egos become bruised.

If Jordan was indeed "one of those people," then what kind of a person did that make me? How had I failed so miserably as a parent? I was somehow guilty of something.

*Guilt*

More than once, I had been on my soapbox proclaiming that if a child went astray, it was the parents' fault. Maybe this was the source of my some of my guilt. I had judged and condemned parents of criminals and addicts, and those who had simply made some bad choices. I had assumed it was bad parenting. I had summarily discounted both free will and addiction.

I stood sanctimoniously in judgment of grieving parents, who had lost their children repeatedly. Then it happened to Jordan, and I fell off my soapbox. I fell hard.

### Stigma

Society makes certain we have a steady stream of shame and guilt, adding stigma, like a cherry on top of our shame and guilt pie. We pile enough shame and guilt on ourselves as parents without anyone adding to it.

We don't choose for our children to become addicts, just as they didn't start out in life planning to become one. Society will tell parents of addicts that they feel sorry for you, but in another breath, they will wonder, "How did you let your kid end up this way?" The stigma that surrounds parents of addicts or those struggling with other issues is suffocating. It is what keeps us in the shadows, rarely reaching out unless it is anonymous.

Several people, upon meeting me or hearing my story have reacted with comments meant to be complimentary toward me. They have said things such as, "I would never have guessed you would have an addict for a child."

Their comments were no doubt meant to express their surprise at how well I appear to be doing in spite of the tragic circumstances. No matter, I can't help but wonder if they half-expect me to have a needle sticking out of my arm.

What do the parents of addicts look like? We look like doctors, lawyers, factory workers, accountants, actors, and receptionists. We look like single moms and dads, Boy Scout leaders, loving parents, struggling parents, softball coaches, and Sunday school teachers. We are blondes, brunettes, and redheads. We have black hair or no hair. Most of us have some gray hair.

We come from all socio-economic groups, ethnic backgrounds, and all cultures. What do parents of addicts look like? We look like you.

There is likely some stigma attached to your Beast, whatever that Beast may be. It is easy for others to judge you or to analyze your actions. People may be quick to offer their critique or to disregard the severity of your pain. It is easy to make a critical judgment about another person's Beast without ever having lived with that Beast.

We all need to work together to shed the shame, guilt and stigma attached to our Beasts.

## In the Belly of Her Beast

One time Jordan contacted me and said she had no food and hadn't eaten since the day before, so I agreed to bring her some food.

Jordan stood outside of a little house with a short white fence, surrounding an overgrown yard. She had attempted to make herself up, but the smeared black eyeliner and bright lipstick didn't hide her declining physical and emotional health. The white top she wore was wrinkled and should have been in the laundry long ago. Her face was broken out, and she had dirt under her fingernails.

Jordan acted like a kid on Christmas when she saw what was in the big tote bags full of food. A teenage boy walked through the little fence and stood playing with an electronic device. They didn't acknowledge one another. I didn't ask who lived in the house, and she didn't offer.

We said we loved each other, and I drove away as she struggled with the bags. I wanted to slam on my brakes, jump out of the car and take her with me, far away from that life. I was finally learning to let go, so instead, I drove away blinking back the tears.

Several of my Supermom rescue attempts included Jordan begging me to allow her to stay in our guest suite, promising she was clean and that this time would be different.

Within a day or two, she would either disappear or be detoxing. If a detox began, she was unwilling for it to continue. Apparently, the only option she or her drug Beast would consider was more drugs. I have heard detoxing from heroin can be likened to having the flu, multiplied by 100. Once a detox begins, an addict knows that all it takes is one hit to stop the pain of withdrawal. No wonder the odds of beating a drug Beast are so low.

I want Jordan to beat the odds; I still believe she can. She is one of the strongest willed people I have ever known. Apparently, the drug addiction Beast is even stronger willed.

With no choice but to return my adult daughter to her drug world, I would drive at first in silence, glancing over at her while she was sweating and beginning to tremble.

As we turned each corner and crossed through intersections, moving closer to our destination, I would try reasoning with her. No amount of pleading would change her mind. Rehab was not an option. There was, but one option she would consider; with which her Beast would agree.

Each time I dropped her off, she turned to me and told me she loved me, and then got out of the car without much more than the clothes on her back. Through tears, I watched in the rearview mirror, as my beloved Jordan made her way across the street and disappeared into the belly of her Beast.

## Losing Me

I am a fairly self-confident person by nature, but after so many failed attempts at saving Jordan from herself, my confidence was all but gone. I became solely focused on Jordan. I went through the motions of life, most of it with a smile on my face that only masked my despair.

For years, I awoke each morning and momentarily looked forward to the day. I no sooner wiped the sleep from my eyes, when the realization hit me - this is my life. I drug myself out of bed and went through the motions of living.

On some days, I was determined to get better, but any hope I found during the day went down with the sun. Days, weeks, months, and years sped by; faster and faster time seemed to move. Rather than becoming stronger, I was losing ground each day.

The people closest to me didn't comprehend the magnitude of my pain; it was a 15 on the Richter scale. Family and friends knew Jordan was shot, and certainly, they understood that Jordan's life was spinning out of control. They heard some of the stories and were eventually made aware that she was addicted to drugs. No doubt, they all felt a certain amount of empathy and sympathy, and those who are parents could only imagine the pain of walking the road of addiction with a child.

Even Rich didn't understand the extent of my sadness. I would cry in my walk-in closet, so as not to upset him. He found me in there on a few occasions. Rich witnessed the black cloud descend upon me out of nowhere and watched me fight to stop it.

Most of what I felt 24 hours a day, I kept to myself. First, I didn't know how to describe the overwhelming ache in my heart. Next, I didn't want to be a burden; for people to feel sorry for me. I was very good at hiding my pain from the world, but I was barely holding it together.

With each milestone that my nieces and nephews reached; graduations, new jobs, college, marriage, children; I was reminded of my loss. Life had become very unfair, and I was fast becoming trapped in victim mode. It may not have shown on the outside, but I was devastated on the inside.

Jordan and one of her cousins had been the best of friends before all hell broke loose. When that cousin was married, it broke my heart that Jordan wasn't in the wedding; she wasn't even at the wedding.

The birth of my grandniece was bittersweet. I was happy for her parents, and for my sister who would have her first grandchild. I was thankful for my family's little miracle. At the same time, I was overcome with sadness. It was on the otherwise joyous day of my grandnieces birth that I presented Jordan with two options: 1) rehab; 2) leaving her grandparents' house and going her own way. She left telling me she would call in three hours; I didn't hear from her for three weeks, and then for months.

It was very difficult to be happy for others when it felt so unfair that I lived on the Roller Coaster From Hell. I tried to focus on the positive and to be happy for others, but the waves of sadness wouldn't stop. As bad as those waves were, the shame and guilt that came crashing in afterward, nearly drowned me.

Life goes on. Life was going on without me. I felt like a stranger in the company of others, even when I was the life of the party. I was putting on a show; that was about to have its last curtain call. I was losing me. You are no doubt losing yourself.

People have confided in me over the years that they have considered suicide. It has never even crossed my mind, yet one day I found myself telling Rich,

"I don't want to be here anymore; it's just too hard."

For most of my life, I didn't understand depression. I had never been depressed for more than an hour. That was before I met my Beast. I'm not certain why I didn't recognize the dark cloud for what it was - depression.

Perhaps my ego didn't want to believe I could be a depressed person. After all, I'm strong and happy by nature. It turns out some of the strongest and naturally happy people I know have been through periods of depression.

I tried to explain to my husband a couple of times how alone I felt, but I didn't even understand it myself. He must have been incredibly sad, and confused, not knowing how to help me not to feel alone, when he was standing right there.

## *Your Beast*

I use "the Beast" in describing our challenges as a way to separate a situation or stronghold, from who we truly are. Your Beast wants to keep you from joy, happiness, courage, and hope; anything and everything that is positive. That is your Beast, but that is not who you are. You are far more than the Beast that is living with you.

You know if you are living with a Beast. It may be that you don't know what to do about it, so you cover your eyes and stick your fingers in your ears, and chant, "La, la, la, la, la." You pretend you don't see the Beast in the room, no matter how many times you run smack into him.

A Beast attacks you in four ways. An attack on one of these will affect the other three.

### 1. Emotionally

When you are living with a Beast, the emotional roller coaster will leave you drained and vacant. Your Beast will work you over until you're heartbroken, sad, depressed, worried, disappointed, confused, overwhelmed, frustrated, and angry - all at the same time.

When you're emotionally drained for an extended period of time, mental paralysis is around the corner. You may begin to experience health issues. Your spirit begins to wither and your faith along with it.

### 2. Mentally

You spend countless hours agonizing over what you could have done differently. If your Beast is attached to another person's, you waste mental energy trying to think your way through their problem, even though you know deep down you have no control over it anyway. You cannot stop thinking about your problem, another person, or the Beast.

Your Beast will keep your mental focus on things that are counterproductive to improving your situation and your life. He will keep you confused and unable to make decisions. Mental paralysis paves the way for unhealthy decisions, contributing to your already compromised emotional, physical, and spiritual well-being.

### 3. Physically

If your Beast can drain your physical energy, he can keep you from thinking clearly. Physically drained, you will be less able to nurture your spirit or to take care of your emotional well-being.

If the Beast has his way, your health will be compromised, ensuring you will have less energy to fight.

### 4. *Spiritually*

The Beast will attack your spirit, distract you from a connection with God, and help to destroy your faith. He cannot afford for you to call in your "Big Gun," so he will do whatever he can to keep you from spiritual peace, maturity, and wisdom.

The Beast is on a mission to destroy your energy, faith, happiness, health, hope, joy, peace, perspective, purpose, relationships, self-confidence, and strength. My Beast nearly completed his mission. Don't let yours win.

## Acknowledging Your Beast

If you are living with a Beast, you know it. Deep down, you realize you're not living the life you were meant to live. Your Beast has you focused on the past, fearful of the future, and unable to live fully in the present.

If you have been living with a Beast for some time, you're beyond tired. The world seems to be turning without you. You are fearful and anxious. Your dreams have all but died. Your self-esteem or self-worth is in the toilet.

It is time to recognize your Beast. You know what it is, and what it's doing to your life. Your Beast is standing right in front of you. It is understandable if he seems larger than life, and you're scared. So, you walk around him, pretending not to notice. Living with this Beast has become your way of life.

I beat a path around mine for years, believing Jordan was the only one with a Beast. I refused to recognize my own.

Don't be concerned that you don't have all of the answers right now. You will figure this out along the way. Your Beast will not be taken down in one move, so don't be concerned that your energy is drained. It's a process, and you will develop the energy, courage, and stamina that it takes to battle your Beast.

In order to begin the battle, it is necessary to identify and acknowledge your Beast. It would be nice if we didn't have to label things, but we do. In order to understand what you are dealing with, you need to name your Beast.

Your Beast may be similar to my two-headed Beast or completely different from mine. Following is a list of <u>possible</u> Beasts. It is by no means a comprehensive list, or an attempt to steer you toward a particular Beast. The list is simply there to help you to understand that nearly everyone has a Beast. You are not alone. It is time to begin identifying your own Beast. Name it and claim it! Check off those characteristics that identify your Beast.

## Name & Claim Your Beast

❏ Addict                    ❏ Perfectionism

❏ Codependency          ❏ Self-Worth (Low)

❏ Control Freak          ❏ _____

❏ Depression              ❏ _____

❏ Domestic Abuse        ❏ _____

❏ Enabling                ❏ _____

❏ Fear                    ❏ _____

**My Beast is:**

**I have been living with my Beast for (how long?)**

**I am ready to make a decision because:**

## Waiting For Someone Else to Change

Often, our life struggle is as a result of somebody else's actions or behavior. We are waiting for them to act or to change, and then our situation will change as a result. It is important to begin accepting the fact that you have no control over anyone but yourself. The problem with waiting for someone else to change before you change is that they may never change!

It is best to focus on helping yourself. If the other person changes on their own or in part because you change, that is wonderful. However, you will live in a constant state of stress and anxiety if you are trying to change another person, waiting for them to change, or thinking that they will automatically change because you begin to take action.

I waited for years for Jordan to stand up to her drug addiction Beast. I figured that once she did, then I could get back to the business of living. That was a huge mistake. I wasted years that I will never get back. Your life's mission, your value, and contribution to society are not tied to another person. Do not let their actions, choices, or lack thereof determine yours.

 **Are you waiting for someone else to change before you take control of your life; before you decide to be happy? If so, who is it and why are you waiting?**

## Comparing Your Beast

We compare things. It allows us to gain perspective on a situation, person, or problem. Be careful when it comes to comparing Beasts. It is not a competition.

You will run into people whose situations don't seem to be as challenging as yours. There will be others who make you feel as if your story pales in comparison to theirs.

Comparing your Beast to another person's Beast is dangerous. If yours appears to be smaller, you will have a tendency to underestimate your situation. It may cause you to minimize your pain and, therefore, not to seek help. When your Beast seems larger than another Beast, you might become insensitive to what another person is going through.

Your Beast is yours alone, and your journey is yours to travel. There will always be another person with a Beast that looms larger than yours. There will always be smaller Beasts. It is best to stay away from the measuring stick when it comes to a Beast.

**It is time to gear up for the battle.**

## Faith in the Battle

As Christian women, we have a unique battle on our hands because the very enemy of our souls will do whatever it takes to cause us to feel worthless and full of self-doubt. Our Beast will preoccupy us with fixing everyone and everything so that we do not even notice we have a Beast or two of our own. As I mentioned earlier, I am the mom of an addict, so it is natural that I struggle with codependency and enabling. I tried to control and fix my son out of desperation to keep him alive. When I pulled on my Supermom Cape, it usually included a heavy dose of "Mom knows best..." The only problem was I was so obsessed with trying to fix my son, I couldn't see that I was losing myself in the process. Pride, shame, and guilt propelled me into an out-of-control world that I was desperately trying to control. I was afraid my son would be stigmatized as a "bad kid," and I would be stigmatized as a bad mother. The truth is I was caught in a trap called "Excuses," and it was time to stop making them. I finally realized I needed to start working on myself. We each have a real enemy who is determined to keep us from being the woman God has called us to be, and he starts by going straight for our hearts. To fight in this battle, you will need to identify your own Beast and the tactics it uses to control you.

 **Look up Ephesians 6:12, and answer these questions:**

**Who is our battle against?**

**What does that battle look like in your life?**

**John 10:10**

**What is the Beast's agenda in our lives?**

**What is the Lord's purpose?**

The Big Beast (Satan) comes to defeat us emotionally, mentally, physically, and spiritually. He uses our Beasts to accomplish his plan to destroy our lives and ruin our relationship with the Lord by trying to make us take our eyes off Him and lock them onto our circumstances. My Beast is a Triple Header as I call it, (Control Freak, Codependent, Enabler). It first attacks me emotionally with fear and panic anytime I receive bad news. Whether something bad happens or not, worry is always crouching at my door! Mentally, I start mulling over the situation, always playing out the worst-case scenario. Physically, my head pounds, I can't sleep, my skin breaks out (ugh), and my neck hurts. Emotionally, I go into control mode; I get angry and bossy. Worst of all are the spiritual attacks. The Beast goes right for the jugular, spewing lies such as, "if you raised your child in the Lord, why is he behaving this way?" or "if you prayed with enough faith and trusted God, why is your child not delivered from his addiction?" No matter what Beast we are each fighting right now, this is not the way God wants us to live, so if we are going to defeat our Beast, we must first battle it on the spiritual level. As we gain spiritual strength, we will become emotionally, mentally, and physically stronger as well.

**Look up the following scriptures and identify ways that your Beast has beat you up:**

**Proverbs 13:12**

**2 Corinthians 11:3**

**Job 2:7**

**Proverbs 18:14**

Learning to see ourselves from God's perspective is a challenge. He knows our heart and our desire to walk by faith. He also sees the obstacles that blind us from seeing the Beasts that have taken us hostage. What appears to be a simple personality defect can paralyze and even destroy us if we let it. Our attempts to help others or even ourselves might be causing more harm than good. The reality that we are living with a Beast may be hard to accept, especially if we have become comfortable living with it. We first need to recognize that something is seriously wrong with how we are living before we can make any real changes. Warning signs that something is awry may include symptoms such as a constant knot in your stomach, a headache, panic attacks, weight gain or loss, or insomnia.  Now, it's time for a little soul searching.

*"Search me, God, and know my heart; test me and know my anxious thoughts. See if there is any offensive way in me, and lead me in the way everlasting."* **Psalm 139:23-24**

 **Ask the Lord to reveal to you any hidden Beasts that you may not be aware of. Go back to the Acknowledging Your Beast Section and modify it if anything new is revealed to you.**

When gearing up for the battle against our Beast, Valerie gave us a very important warning against falling into the comparison trap. Comparing keeps us so "other focused" that we are blinded to what the Lord is revealing in our own situations. The Bible also warns us against judging another person. We have yet to walk in their shoes.  I believe this goes both ways. Sometimes, we judge ourselves more harshly than we should. We refuse to give ourselves the same consideration we would give another person going through this battle.  If we are choosing to be free from our Beasts, we will need to become aware of the lies we believe when we fall into the comparison trap.

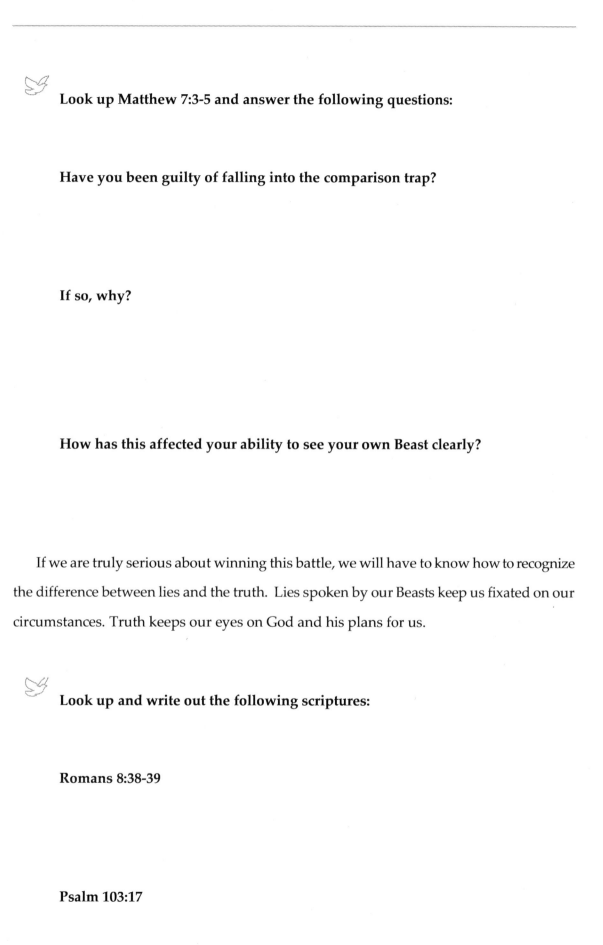

**Look up Matthew 7:3-5 and answer the following questions:**

**Have you been guilty of falling into the comparison trap?**

**If so, why?**

**How has this affected your ability to see your own Beast clearly?**

If we are truly serious about winning this battle, we will have to know how to recognize the difference between lies and the truth. Lies spoken by our Beasts keep us fixated on our circumstances. Truth keeps our eyes on God and his plans for us.

**Look up and write out the following scriptures:**

**Romans 8:38-39**

**Psalm 103:17**

What are practical ways you can "let go and trust the Lord" in your own life personally and the lives of the people you care for?

Write a prayer for yourself, asking God to renew your strength and provide you with wisdom and courage for this battle. This would be a good time to also include prayers for loved ones that you have been struggling with and may need to let go of and give to the Lord.

*"The greatest moments in life are the miraculous moments when human impotence and divine omnipotence intersect-and they intersect when we draw a circle around the impossible situations in our lives and invite God to intervene."*
**-Mark Batterson - The Circle Maker**

## *Action #1: Decide to Stand Up and Fight*

"Life is short, and it is getting shorter every day. Today is the day, not tomorrow, not someday. TODAY is the day to stand up and Battle Your Beast."

—*Valerie Silveira*

## Action Introduction

We take hundreds of small actions every day, and major ones less frequently. Actions such as taking a shower don't take a great deal of conscious thought while a life changing decision such as a career or marriage might take months of thought. Whether it's a simple or a major decision, all actions are preceded by thoughts. Before you take an action, you make a decision.

Some of the most important decisions we can make, those that can change our lives for the better, are the most difficult to make. Real change takes work, and most people either don't want to change or don't want to go through the uncomfortable process of change.

How many times have you made a New Year's Resolution that didn't last through January? In order for your life to change for the better, you will need to take serious and consistent action. Before any action can be taken, you must first make a decision.

You are reading this book because there is something that is holding you back from being happy, at peace, or living with hope. You are feeling helpless or heartbroken. You live with shame and guilt. You are angry, resentful, frustrated, and confused. You want to have a better attitude and focus on the right things, but you're obsessed with someone or something. You are mentally, emotionally, physically, and spiritually drained. You may be living in paralyzing fear or waiting for someone to change so your life can change.

If you can relate to one or many of these thoughts and emotions, it is time for you to make a decision. I felt as if this "thing" had control over me and I was clueless as to how to battle it. As a drug addict, my daughter is living with a Beast. As a Codependent Enabler, I too was living with a Beast. They come in many forms, and only you know what kind of Beast is living with you. Only you can make the decision to stand up and fight.

## Pivotal Decision

Decide the time is now, and you're worth whatever it takes to get there. Decide you're *all in,* and you will stay in the battle no matter how long it takes, or how challenging it becomes.

You have probably tried taking action before, and possibly, you are taking some action now. When you finally decide you're going to stand up no matter how many times you are knocked down, it will be a pivotal decision.

Once I made my decision and began to use the very actions in this book on a daily basis, everything in my life began to change - fast. I will not tell you it has been smooth sailing, but at least I finally had a roadmap. Over the years, I had wandered around attempting to employ pieces and parts of each Action. It wasn't until I got them all working to some degree simultaneously, that I began to realize massive change.

There were many factors involved in my decision. One major factor was the realization that I have zero control over whether or not Jordan battles her Beast, let alone beats it. I had to face the harsh reality that in my lifetime, I might not see Jordan take control of her Beast.

I was standing at a crossroads, beaten down and not sure which way to turn. Up ahead in the road that I was already on was more of the same. The other choice was to take whatever energy I had left and head down the other road - the one that led to freedom from my Beast.

There I stood staring down the road of despair, the road I knew all too well. I looked over at the road to freedom and saw roadblocks, mountains, and monsters. I knew it would be a challenge, but I was done with the other road.

It was my choice; nobody was going to make it for me. Before I took a step forward, I hesitated. It felt as if I was leaving Jordan behind on that road of despair. Truthfully, Jordan had already left me. So, I made a decision - it was time to take my life back. That is just what I did.

You too are standing at a crossroads. It is time for you to take your life back.

## Stand Up

My son, Sean played many different sports, most of them team sports. As a parent, the most nerve-wracking sport to watch was wrestling. Although wrestling is an individual sport, it's also a team sport. Sean was in the heavyweight division, and it was always the final match, and sometimes the deciding match, to see which team would win. The spotlight was on the lone mat and two heavyweight wrestlers.

At tournaments, in the early elimination matches, several mats were laid out with multiple matches going on at the same time. Family and friends were allowed to stand by the mats during those early matches.

Rich and I stood near the mat during one such tournament. This particular match pitted Sean against a very strong and more experienced opponent. Sean started the round in the down position, on all fours. His opponent had a tight hold on him as Sean struggled to get up. He was on his feet, but unable to fully stand up.

His coach paced nervously while the two boys struggled; Sean to free himself, and his opponent to take him down to the mat. As he paced, the coach yelled until he was red in the face,

"Stand up Sean! Stand up!"

I had visions of Sean's back going out if he tried any harder to stand up with a very heavy guy on him. I was about to say something to the coach when Rich gently grabbed my arm. Eventually, despite his opponent's efforts to drop him to the mat, Sean stood up and ultimately won the match. His coach knew he didn't stand much of a chance unless Sean found a way to stand up.

My Beast had me down on the mat; I was heartbroken, terrified, and exhausted. My Codependent Enabler Beast was strong, and I was becoming emotionally, spiritually and mentally weaker by the day. My decision to stand up quite possibly saved my life.

You may be down on the mat, with your Beast on top of you. If you don't stand up, you too will be pinned. Just as Sean's coach yelled at him, I'm yelling at you (in love),

"Stand up!"

 **Who else is yelling for you to Stand Up?**

## The World Keeps Turning

Jordan spent her late teens and her twenties in the belly of her Beast, detached from her family. She missed nearly every Christmas and Thanksgiving, and all birthdays, including her own. There was an empty seat at family dinners and a hole in my heart at family gatherings.

Jordan's Beast caused her to miss the weddings of three cousins, and the birth of one of their babies. She missed the memorial services of her aunt and her beloved grandfather.

Her drug Beast kept her from the family that could support her recovery. Sadly, my Beast kept me from enjoying much of those same years and made sure I felt like an outsider, even when surrounded by people who love me.

 **Do you feel as if, in some way, the world is turning without you?**

## Precious Time

When you allow a Beast to continue to consume you, essentially you are giving away your precious time. Consider how much time you have already spent feeling as if the world is spinning without you; all of the time you can never recover.

Imagine for a moment that when you were born, you knew the exact number of days you would live. How would you choose to spend your allotted time? When you were younger, it seemed as if you had nothing but time left. The older we get, time seems to move more quickly, but, of course, time keeps moving at the same speed it has always moved. It is simply the closer we get to the inevitable; we begin to recognize the value of precious time. The saying goes: "time flies when you're having fun." I disagree - time flies whether you're having fun or not.

 **Answer the following questions:**

1. **Has your Beast kept you from participating in your life?**

2. **Do you spend a lot of time feeling anxious?**

3. **If so, what are you anxious about?**

4. **Have you found yourself questioning when "this will end"?**

5. **Do you feel stuck as if life is going on without you?**

6. **Is it possible for you to control or change the person or situation you are caught up in?**

7. **If you don't have control, are you waiting for someone else to resolve a situation or make changes, in order to change your life for the better?**

8. **If you have control over it, why have you not chosen to make changes?**

9. **If it is a situation beyond your control (e.g. a loved one who is an addict, a loved one who has left you, a situation that happened in the past), do you want to learn to rise above it?**

On the chart below, locate the line in the "Years" column that represents the number of years you have been living with your Beast.

| Years | Months | Days | Hours | Minutes |
|---:|---:|---:|---:|---:|
| 1 | 12 | 365 | 8,760 | 525,600 |
| 2 | 24 | 730 | 17,520 | 1,051,200 |
| 3 | 36 | 1,095 | 26,280 | 1,576,800 |
| 4 | 48 | 1,460 | 35,040 | 2,102,400 |
| 5 | 60 | 1,825 | 43,800 | 2,628,000 |
| 6 | 72 | 2,190 | 52,560 | 3,153,600 |
| 7 | 84 | 2,555 | 61,320 | 3,679,200 |
| 8 | 96 | 2,920 | 70,080 | 4,204,800 |
| 9 | 108 | 3,285 | 78,840 | 4,730,400 |
| 10 | 120 | 3,650 | 87,600 | 5,256,000 |
| 11 | 132 | 4,015 | 96,360 | 5,781,600 |
| 12 | 144 | 4,380 | 105,120 | 6,307,200 |
| 13 | 156 | 4,745 | 113,880 | 6,832,800 |
| 14 | 168 | 5,110 | 122,640 | 7,358,400 |
| 15 | 180 | 5,475 | 131,400 | 7,884,000 |
| 16 | 192 | 5,840 | 140,160 | 8,409,600 |
| 17 | 204 | 6,205 | 148,920 | 8,935,200 |
| 18 | 216 | 6,570 | 157,680 | 9,460,800 |
| 19 | 228 | 6,935 | 166,440 | 9,986,400 |
| 20 | 240 | 7,300 | 175,200 | 10,512,000 |
| 21 | 252 | 7,665 | 183,960 | 11,037,600 |
| 22 | 264 | 8,030 | 192,720 | 11,563,200 |
| 23 | 276 | 8,395 | 201,480 | 12,088,800 |
| 24 | 288 | 8,760 | 210,240 | 12,614,400 |
| 25 | 300 | 9,125 | 219,000 | 13,140,000 |

- **How many <u>Years</u> have you have been living with your Beast?**

- **How many <u>Months</u> have you have been living with your Beast?**

- **How many <u>Days</u> have you have been living with your Beast?**

- **How many <u>Hours</u> have you have been living with your Beast?**

- **How many <u>Minutes</u> have you have been living with your Beast?**

Although the figures are on the chart, there is something about writing them down that makes it more real. I lived with my Beast for nearly 13 years or 156 months. Think for a moment about how quickly a month goes by. I gave away 4,745 days, trapped in a cycle of hope and disappointment, and 113,880 hours living in paralyzing fear. Over 6 million minutes flew by while I allowed my Beast to convince me that unless my daughter's life changed drastically, that mine was pretty much over.

**How did you feel about the number of years, months, days, and minutes that you have spent living with your Beast?**

 **With time seemingly moving faster, how much more time are you willing to spend before you decide enough is enough?**

## The *"Why"* in the Road

Humans want to know how things work, and why they are the way they are. Those questions have led to advancements in technology, science, medicine, and psychology. When life throws you a curveball, you will ask "why" in a way you have never asked before. It moves far beyond curiosity, to a desperate need to understand why this is happening to you.

When Jordan's Beast grabbed hold of her, I began to ask why. Why me? Why my daughter? Why my family? Why did Jordan become a drug addict? Why was she drawn out of her beautiful, wonderful, safe, happy life and into this dark place? Why won't she stop? Why did she have to be shot? Why can't I make her stop using drugs? Why am I the only one feeling this way right now? Why is everybody else enjoying their lives? Why me?

Finally, I asked myself this: Why not me?

Consider the possibility that your obstacle, pain, or heartbreak could be a catalyst for good. The very thing that nearly took you down could be the situation that propels you to a place you never imagined. The Beast you lived with for so long could be the very thing that gives you a unique perspective on the lives of others. What has occurred may not be fair, but since it's a reality, why not take your pain and decide to find meaning in the madness?

 **Why not you? Why not be the person who overcomes?**

## If You Can't Do It For Yourself

Making the decision to stand up and fight will require energy, commitment, stamina, a good attitude, and much more. It may seem as if you don't have the courage right now to take the first step, let alone put all of the pieces of your broken life back together.

In a sense, I had accepted a life sentence. I had come to believe my best days were behind me, and it was not possible for me to be happy again until Jordan beat her Beast. I was defeated, and although I stood at the crossroads, knowing I needed to choose life, I wasn't sure I could do it - for myself.

I found the courage to stand initially because of, and for, my son. He had been through enough - losing his first friend and his only sibling to the drug addiction Beast, and then slowly losing his mother. It pained me to think that one day Sean would be forced to describe his mom as a sad, lonely woman. I didn't want to miss an opportunity to show my son that even in your darkest hour, it's possible to stand up and fight. At the time, I found it much easier to fight for someone else's sake than my own.

Initially, I stood up to fight, mainly because of Sean. When I was knocked down again, I stood up because my husband deserved to get back the woman he married. Each time I stood up to my Beast, I gained a little bit more of my self-worth back, and today I stand because I'm worth it.

You have been beaten down, and might feel as I did, that it's easier to stay down on the mat than to find the last shred of self-worth or confidence you might have left. One way or another, it's time for you to get back up off the mat; to stand up and fight. If at first, you cannot do it for yourself, do it for someone you love. Just do it.

 **If at first, you can't do it for yourself, write down the names of the people in your life for whom you can stand.**

## Fight as if Your Life Depends on It

Nobody ever said life was going to be easy. Life can be sad, painful, and heartbreaking. I could have never imagined my brilliant daughter would wind up being shot by a gang member or addicted to drugs. My future looked bright at the time all hell broke loose. Your Beast may have blindsided you.

I have asked Jordan why she doesn't stand up and battle her Beast. Her answer is that it is harder than I realize. I am sure a drug addiction Beast is hard to battle. I witnessed Jordan detoxing a few times, and it was horrible. I've read grim statistics on heroin addiction recovery, which are enough to make me roll into a ball and cry.

Jordan's path to life must seem nearly insurmountable. However, staying in her addiction will mean death, so her only real option is to fight as if her life depends on it because it does.

My Beast sucked the very life out of me and had me down on the mat with his claws around my throat. I was beginning to exist, rather than to live.

Have you lost your joy, hope, peace, self-confidence, and your sense of value? Are you obsessed with your Beast or somebody or with something that is causing you anguish and heartbreak? Is your life out of focus? Are you missing out on meaningful relationships, afraid to give or receive love? Are you pretending to be happy when you don't feel happy? Do you feel as if you're not really living?

There is a big difference between the noun, living, and the adjective, *living*!

 **Be determined to fight this battle as if your life depends on it because it does. Are you ready?**

 **Check off all of the emotions & issues you currently identify with:**

| | | |
|---|---|---|
| ❑ Angry | ❑ Grief-constant | ❑ Out of Balance |
| ❑ Anxious | ❑ Guilty | ❑ Relationship Issues |
| ❑ Confused | ❑ Isolated | ❑ Resentment |
| ❑ Controlling | ❑ Jealous | ❑ Sadness |
| ❑ Denial | ❑ Lack of confidence | ❑ Sleep Issues |
| ❑ Depressed | ❑ Lack of self-worth | ❑ Stuck |
| ❑ Disappointed | ❑ Lonely | ❑ Unable to Focus |
| ❑ Exhausted | ❑ Loss of Faith | ❑ Unappreciated |
| ❑ Fatigued | ❑ Loss of Hope | ❑ Unhappy |
| ❑ Fearful | ❑ Loss of Joy | ❑ Unwilling to Forgive |
| ❑ Financial Issues | ❑ Negative Attitude | ❑ Unworthy |
| ❑ Frustrated | ❑ No Sense of Purpose | ❑ Victim |
| ❑ Giving-up | ❑ Obsessed | ❑ Worried |

**Check off the emotions and states of mind that you look forward to:**

- ❏ Alive
- ❏ Appreciated
- ❏ Balanced
- ❏ Capable
- ❏ Confident
- ❏ Courageous
- ❏ Faithful
- ❏ Fearless
- ❏ Focused
- ❏ Forgiving
- ❏ Happy
- ❏ Happy for Others
- ❏ Healthy Relationships
- ❏ Hopeful
- ❏ In-Control
- ❏ Joyful
- ❏ Loved
- ❏ Peaceful
- ❏ Positive Attitude
- ❏ Rested
- ❏ Self-Love
- ❏ Sense of Purpose
- ❏ Strong
- ❏ Worthy

## Staying in the Ring

*"The battle is over when you say it is over. Stay in the Ring until the final round. Commit to staying in the fight until you are standing over your Beast."*
— *Valerie Silveira*

Anytime you are making a life change; there will be setbacks. Some days it will feel as if you take a step forward, only to take a step back. On other days, you will take one-step forward and two steps back. Eventually, you will begin to take two steps forward and only one-step back.

As with any positive, life-changing endeavor, when you begin to take action, the forces of darkness will work to derail you. The harder you fight your Beast, the harder he will fight back.

There will be days when you are knocked down - it's inevitable. Don't become discouraged when that happens, just stand back up, dust yourself off, and keep battling. Your Beast can knock you down as many times as he likes, but as long as you get up more times than you are knocked down, eventually you will prevail.

 **Will you commit to staying in the ring until the final round?**

## Fitting the Pieces Together

The Nine Actions to Battle Your Beast can be focused on independently, yet each one is dependent upon the others. With all of the Actions working together, you will begin to put the pieces back together after all hell has broken loose.

Your decision to stand up and fight is critical to the process of putting the pieces of your life back together. Without a serious decision, you will probably quit when the going gets tough. Each time you meet with a challenge, remember you made a decision to battle your Beast, no matter how long it takes or how hard the battle becomes.

Changing old habits and behaviors takes time. When heartbreak is a part of your battle, it is more challenging. Ask yourself how challenging it has been to live with the Beast! Taking control will empower you, and little by little, you will gain the strength, courage, and wisdom you need to take your Beast down.

1. When you **Decide to Stand Up and Fight**, you are making the decision to work on the other eight Actions:
2. Get On Your Spiritual Armor
3. Put On Your Oxygen Mask
4. Build Your Circle of Strength
5. Change Your Attitude

6. Adjust Your Focus

7. Stop Being a Control Freak

8. Stand <u>On</u> Your Story

9. Make Meaning From the Madness

## Your Declaration

Complete the blanks in the Decide to Stand Up & Fight declaration. Read it aloud every day for as long as it takes for you to be *all in*. As you work through the Actions, you might find yourself becoming discouraged or derailed. When that happens, go back to the Declaration and read it out loud. You may need to re-decide from time to time.

---

**<u>Decide to Stand Up & Fight Declaration</u>**

I, _____ am in a battle with a Beast. My Beast is: _____

_____

Today, _____, 20_____ I will **Stand Up** and Battle My Beast. I know that I will be knocked down, but I declare that I will get up every time, and that I will take my life back no matter how long it takes, or how difficult the Battle may become. I am a warrior.

_____
Signed

---

## Faith in the Battle

*"Today I have given you the choice between life and death, between blessings and curses.*

*Now I will call on heaven and earth to witness the choice you make.*

*Oh, that you would choose life, so that you and your descendants might live!"*

**Deuteronomy 30:19 NLT**

By the time I decided to stand up and fight, I barely recognized myself. Where once I was a strong and confident person, now I felt anxious and even jumped when the telephone rang. No matter how I occupied myself, I could think of only one thing, my addicted son. Finally, enough was enough. I was no longer willing to obsess over things I had no control over. The realization that I had spent too much time and effort worrying about things I was powerless to control came at a big price…my sanity. Valerie wrote earlier in the chapter, "time flies whether you're having fun or not." Time is precious so why waste it worrying? I had dreams the Lord had given me for my life. When I thought about them, they brought me joy, but also frustration. I honestly believed God was ready to move me into a new chapter in my life. My "stand-up" moment came when I realized there was no moving forward as long as my feet were tethered to my son's addiction Beast and my Beasts had my hands cuffed behind my back! No more wasting precious time. I resolved to stand up and fight and get my life back.

 **Meditate on this scripture verse and answer the following questions.**

*"For I know the plans I have for you,"* declares the Lord, *"plans to prosper you and not to harm you, plans to give you hope and a future."* **Jeremiah 29:11**

What dreams and plans have you put on a shelf because of living with your Beast?

Do you believe those plans were placed in your heart by the Lord for a reason?

If your Beast was no longer an issue in your life, would there be anything else hindering you from moving forward with your plans and goals?

Look up the following scriptures and note how they speak to you personally:

Psalm 37:4

**Proverbs 16:3**

**Proverbs 3:5-6**

Why? Why my child? These questions haunted me day and night, yet the answers never came. I believed I was somehow to blame and had I not been asleep at the wheel; I could have prevented my son's addiction. My head told me there was nothing I could have done, but my heart told me otherwise. Still, there was one question that plagued me more than any other. Why did God allow this to happen to my son when He most certainly could have prevented it? Ouch! With a bruised ego and weakened faith, I could find no answer that brought me any relief. Then the Lord gently reminded me.

*"For my thoughts are not your thoughts, neither are your ways my ways," declares the Lord. "As the heavens are higher than the earth, so are my ways higher than your ways and my thoughts than your thoughts."* **Isaiah 55:8-9**

We all have "whys" in our lives that demand answers we are unable to give. We are tormented with the "hows" as well. "How did this happen? How will it turn out?" We may never have the answers to all the "whys" and "hows" in our lives, but we know that Jesus does. The One who suffered beyond our understanding holds our brokenness in his wounded hands and promises to still the storm in our hearts if we will just let go, trust him and stand, even if the answers never come.

Valerie asked us earlier in the chapter to write down the names of the people who we are willing to stand and fight for. Even if I felt I could not do it for myself or anyone else, I had to do it because the Lord wanted me to. He never asks us to do anything without His help. He is willing to fight this battle in us and with us.

*"Have I not commanded you? Be strong and courageous. Do not be afraid; do not be discouraged, for the Lord your God will be with you wherever you go."* **Joshua 1:9 NIV**

**Look up the following scripture and write it out.**

**Nehemiah 4:14**

**Who does the Lord tell you to fight for? Remember, you are not fighting this battle alone.**

Earlier, Valerie encouraged us to fight as if our lives depended on it (and they do). This reminds me of Lot's wife in the story of Sodom and Gomorrah in Genesis 19. As the Lord rained down burning sulfur on the condemned city, Lot and his family fled their fiery home with two warnings from the angels the Lord had sent to save them. "Flee for your lives and don't look back!" Reluctant to flee the cursed city, Lot's wife disobeyed the command and turned back for one last look. Instantly, she became a pillar of salt. (vs.26) Like stone, she became stuck, lifeless and immovable. She was so tied to her past, good and bad, and the safety of her comfort zone that she could not believe God had something "better" in store for her. As a result, she lost everything she clung so tightly to, including her very life.

Speaking of being stuck, this reminds me of song that is at the top of my "Most Hated Songs" list. It is that old hit song by the Eagles called "Hotel California," and it creeps me out for a number of reasons, mainly for one line that goes like this. "You can check out any time you want, but you can never leave." When my Beast had me down on the mat, I felt caught in a time-warp with concrete up to my knees and those lyrics playing over and over again. Every day was Groundhog Day. I was stuck in my own head and risked becoming a pillar of salt if I didn't do something drastic. I finally got unstuck when I started looking ahead instead of at my present seemingly hopeless circumstances. God wants us to be free to live the life He has planned for us. He does not want us stuck or held back by our Beasts. Let's look closer at what the following scriptures say about being stuck.

**Look up Isaiah 43:18-19.**

**What are we told to do in verse 18?**

**What is the Lord's promise to us in verse 19?**

**Look up Galatians 5:1:**

**Why did Christ set us free?**

**How are we instructed in this verse to live?**

**Do you feel encouraged to move forward as you read these verses?**

Today is the day you can choose to stand and fight. Make the decision to stand and fight as if your life depends on it. Remember, you are not alone in this battle. God is fighting for you, and with his help, you are guaranteed to win the battle over your Beast.

*"We are all faced with a series of great opportunities brilliantly disguised as impossible situations."*

*-Charles Swindoll*

## _Action #2: Get On Your Spiritual Armor_

_"Having faith is not a sign of weakness. When you are in a battle, it is wise to bring your "big gun."_

— **Valerie Silveira**

## Action Introduction

As much as we desire to trust in others, there can be a fear of being let down or duped. At some point in your life, somebody has been untruthful, taken advantage of you or made a fool of you. Once you experience mistrust, it leaves you skeptical.

That same fear can hold us back from having faith in a higher power. What if you believe something that turns out not to be true? Worse yet, what will people think if you have certain spiritual beliefs that differ from theirs.

The last thing you should concern yourself with is what others think. When your time is up, wherever you go, you will be standing there alone. Your friends, family or coworkers will not be there pointing at you and laughing because you got it wrong. Why are we so concerned with what other people think of our spiritual beliefs? Your spiritual connection is between you and your God. In the end, it will only matter to you if you got it right.

We will move forward with the assumption that good and evil exist. You can choose to refer to these spiritual forces in whatever way makes you most comfortable. I am going to use God as our higher power, our maker, our collective spiritual source of energy and all that is good. Satan represents the opposite of God and the source of all evil. However, I have given Satan a nickname - he is the Big Beast.

 **What are your personal spiritual beliefs?**

 **In what ways will God help you in your battle?**

## Body, Mind, and Spirit

You are made up of body, mind, and spirit, but how much time do you really commit to nurturing your spirit?

Our bodies get a lot of attention. We go to the gym, wear makeup, go to the hair salon, and fill our closets with clothing. Some people go to the extent of having cosmetic surgery. We are inundated with the latest fad diets. Every other day, another study comes out about which foods are good for us, and which are not and each one contradicts the last. We feed, clothe, moisturize, satisfy, tighten, lift, energize, medicate and rest, our bodies. We are obsessed with our bodies in one way or another.

We hunger for knowledge and gladly feed that hunger. The brain processes a constant stream of information and stimuli. In today's technologically advanced world of instant information, our brains are bombarded, nonstop.

Often, it's our spirit we ignore. When your heart is aching, you may try to think your way through the minefield.

If your situation lasts over an extended period, you might even be mad at God. I'm not afraid to admit that I have been mad at, disappointed in, and frustrated with God. The problem with getting to that point is your spiritual strength is critical to your battle and helps to support your mental and emotional strength.

Your spirit is your heart and soul. Don't put it in last place.

 **Do you spend enough time nurturing your spirit?**

 **If not, what can you do to spend more time and energy with God & strengthening your spirit?**

## Beasts Are Tough, But God Is Tougher

If there is a school of Beasts, you can bet the Big Beast is the headmaster. Never underestimate the power of the Big Beast, and, therefore, the power of your Beast. Keep the armor of God on at all times.

Your Beast will beat you up physically. You are an emotional wreck. Mentally, you are drained; trying to understand what is happening and attempting to figure out what to do about it.

In the darkest days of my journey, I couldn't put two thoughts together and was on the verge of tears every moment, and I was physically exhausted. During these times, it was my connection with God that gave me the strength to keep going.

It is what will allow you to keep going when you think you can't take another step. Beasts are tough, but God is tougher. God is your Big Gun in the battle with your Beast.

 **Have you experienced the Big Beast stepping up his game the more you attempt to increase your faith?**

## Faith Over Fear

Faith is never more tested than when you are on the Roller Coaster From Hell, riding in the dark with a Beast, terrified of what is around the next corner.

An acronym for fear is:

**F**alse

**E**vidence

**A**ppearing

**R**eal

Most of what we end up worrying about never happens. Fear is essential to survival and keeps us alert to danger, but excess fear can be paralyzing. Fear is exhausting on every level. It takes a greater amount of energy to live in fear than to step out in faith.

**"Only when we are no longer afraid do we begin to live."**
**— Dorothy Thompson, Journalist**

I have a fear of heights. Standing at the edge of a cliff or next to a window in a skyscraper makes me physically ill. I highly doubt you will ever catch me jumping out of an airplane or bungee jumping.

Many years ago, I went on a quest to conquer my fear of heights. I went in a hot air balloon and flew in a small airplane from Scottsdale to the Grand Canyon.

I went hiking to the top of Mt. Pilchuck and stood out on a rock outside of the lookout building. I had hiked the same mountain before and bravely climbed the ladder to the lookout, but had to climb right back down to solid ground. This time, I walked around the outside deck of the tiny lookout, stepped through a break in the railing and onto a plank leading to the rock in this photo.

Fear isn't always rational. Clearly, there is little chance I will fall out of the window of a skyscraper, yet it still scares me. Many people are terrified of air travel. Statistically, there is a far greater chance of dying in a car on the way to the airport than in an airplane crash. However, people who have a fear of flying continue to hop in their car every day without giving it a thought, and still require a tranquilizer before boarding an airplane.

Fear is the opposite of faith, and it's not from God; it's one of the battle tactics the Big Beast uses to separate you from God. The more you give in to your fears, the more control the Beast has over you.

To the contrary, fear backs down when you face it. The Beast backs down when you stand up to him. When you're wearing your spiritual armor, the Beast shudders.

Face those fears! Recognize you're scared, but stand strong in the face of fear. The more you stand up to your fears, the less fearful you will be.

Although there is no guarantee that when you live in faith, your battle will be easier, just imagine what condition you would be in without faith.

 **Without giving thought to how rational or not your fears may be, list the 5 things that you fear most:**

1.

2.

3.

4.

5.

- Circle the number next to each Fear that you have no significant control over.

- Put a check mark next to each Fear that you have had for some time that has not happened.

- Place a line through all Fears that are, for the most part, completely out of your control.

- Finally, put a big circle around any Fear that you have been living with for the longest time, or the one that you Fear the most.

Sit back and take a look at your list of five Fears. If you are like most people, your list will be a big mess of circles, strikethroughs, and check marks!

 **Think about something that you were very worried about that turned out fine. It doesn't matter if it's something trivial or something big. The lesson is the same. What was it?**

 **How did it turn out?**

**List all of the ways in which worrying about this situation helped the outcome.** I purposely didn't leave you any room for this one. There are times when we need to be genuinely concerned. That is very different from worry. Worrying NEVER changes the outcome of anything.

Jesus said, "Can any one of you by worrying add a single hour to your life?" He also told us, "Therefore do not worry about tomorrow, for tomorrow will worry about itself. Each day has enough trouble of its own."

## Faith When You're Not Feeling It

When Jordan went off the rails, and I couldn't get her back on track, my faith was tested. My faith wavered as Jordan lay in a hospital bed with a bullet in her abdomen, and I stood in the hallway yelling at God. The realization that she was a heroin addict and that I was powerless to stop her no matter how many times I prayed caused my faith to be shaken.

My faith has been tested, just as yours has. I will not mislead you into thinking I have had some superhuman faith through it all. To be truthful, I kept seeking God simply because I didn't know what else to do.

 **How has your faith been tested?**

 **How do you stay in faith when you don't feel the presence of God?**

## Faith When the Teacher Is Silent

"Not only so, but we also glory in our sufferings, because we know that

suffering produces perseverance; perseverance, character; and character,

hope."

*(Romans 5:3-4)*

The turning point in your faith might well happen when you feel as if you have nothing left. There have been extended periods of time where I couldn't hear from or feel God's presence at all; nothing, zip, zilch. These situations caused me a tremendous amount of confusion, distress, and fear. I am not a very "religious" person, and I am not super comfortable being demonstrative when I go to church, but alone I dropped to the floor many times begging to hear from God.

It seemed that at times the more I sought God, the quieter he became. I cried out to him like a mad woman, but the silence continued. I tried to figure out what I was doing wrong and why God wouldn't show himself to me when I was trying so hard to find him.

I learned the teacher is often silent while the student is taking a test. In those times when you feel far from God, do not panic, it may be only a test.

**What are the things that you can do TODAY to live in faith?**

## Patience

We all have our strengths. Unfortunately, we all have weaknesses; one of mine is patience, and it has caused me unnecessary stress over the years. Impatience creates frustration, intolerance and a great deal of disappointment. I had always admired people who had an abundance of patience.

Right around the time all hell broke loose, I got down on my knees, and boldly asked God for patience, and then I got back up and waited. To this day, I'm not exactly sure what I was waiting for, but I must have assumed I would simply start being patient. After all, before I put in my request, I did admit my weakness, apologized and asked for forgiveness. What more could I do?

It seemed as if I had no sooner asked for patience when all hell broke loose. Upon hearing my request, God didn't think, "I know how to force Valerie to become patient; I will allow her only daughter to take up with a gang member and survive a near-fatal gunshot wound, only to become an addict. I will make sure she goes through a lot of pain and heartbreak. Yep, that should help her develop patience."

No, that is not how it went, but in his infinite wisdom, God knew what the future would hold for Jordan, and he used it to help me to develop more patience.

I will never be the most patient person in the world; it's not in my DNA, but I'm a hundred times more patient than I was the day I put in my petition. My prayer was answered, but not in the way I had expected.

I hope I didn't scare you off from asking for patience. It is not developed overnight, and without pain, but it's worth it. You will have to do your part to develop patience, and it has a great deal to do with faith.

 **Are you ready to go through what you might need to go through in order to develop patience?**

It is quite possible that you have already been through enough to develop patience to last two lifetimes! Most of us can use more patience, no matter how much patience we have managed to develop.

 **Can you think of ways in which your lack of patience in certain situations only made the situation more challenging?**

 **What are some tangible ways in which you could work to develop more patience? Go over the list below and check off any that you are willing to put effort toward. Add any in the open boxes that are not on this list.**

## Developing Patience

| | |
|---|---|
| ❑ Breathe | ❑ Remember I'm not perfect |
| ❑ Consider another perspective | ❑ Slow down |
| ❑ Let go (see Action #7: Stop Being a Control Freak | ❑ Understand everyone has different gifts and abilities |
| ❑ Lighten up | ❑ Understand my timing might not be God's timing |
| ❑ Put myself in others' shoes | ❑ _____ |
| ❑ Put the current situation in perspective | ❑ _____ |

## The Frantic Quest For Peace

Frantic is not exactly the word that comes to mind when one thinks of peace, but it helps to illustrate just how important it is to strive for peace.

Too often, the level of peace we experience is in direct proportion to how well things are going in our lives. Hardship, heartbreak, disappointment, and troubles will hit all people to varying degrees. They are unavoidable; a part of the deal that comes with living on planet earth. The key is to come to a place where you can find peace during times of trouble.

The world may tell you that you have no right to feel peace in the midst of your storm - don't listen to the world. The Big Beast will try to convince you that as a parent, you cannot possibly be at peace when your child is headed for disaster - don't listen to the Big Beast. Your Beast will reason with you that you can't afford to be peaceful, that you need to stay on high alert - turn away from your Beast. You have every right to be at peace, even in the eye of the storm. God offers you the gift of peace that surpasses all understanding. Unfortunately, most of us are not good receivers of this gift.

I came to the realization that life with a drug addict could mean that the storm would never cease. That reality helped spark my frantic quest for peace. If I had no control over the circumstances, then I needed to gain control over how I reacted to them.

Finding this kind of peace will require you to give up control and to put your faith and trust in God, in hopes that peace will help you to weather the storm.

When all hell breaks loose, your natural tendency will be to attempt to control the situation. I have given it to God many times, only to begin giving him pointers. It's like saying,

"I know you've got this God, but here are some bullet points, just in case."

My frantic quest for peace has turned out to be pretty miraculous considering the control freak I had become. I am not at a place where I'm sitting on an island, my feet in the sand and a smile on my face while the sharks swarm around me, as depicted in this image. I still feel a raindrop or two and every now and again the clouds darken my heart, but I'm getting there. I hope you do too.

 **Can you think of a time when you were peaceful, yet it didn't seem reasonable considering your circumstances? What were the circumstances?**

♥ **Why do you think you had peace when it seemed as if you shouldn't?**

♥ **How might you begin to find that type of peace in your current situation?**

♥ **Here are some tips for developing peace. Add your ideas in the blank spaces.**

☐ Praying for peace.

☐ Breathing exercises or meditation.

☐ Reciting scripture.

☐ Work on being more patient.

☐ Forgiving yourself.

☐ Forgiving others. Who? _____

☐ Studying the Bible or other spiritual materials.

☐ Reading and internalizing positive quotes, thoughts, & wisdom.

☐ Speaking encouragement over yourself.

☐ _____

☐ _____

☐ _____

## Stop Looking For Your Crystal Ball

We want answers; we demand them. One of the questions that will play again in your mind is, "When will all of this be over?"

For three years, I kept wondering what Jordan would have to experience in order for things to change, for her to return to the Jordan she was before all hell broke loose.

When Jordan was shot, I thought for certain things couldn't get worse. That was in 2004, and things got a hell of a lot worse after the shooting. I spent the better part of the next decade asking the same question, "When will all of this be over?"

The reality is nobody knows the answer to that question. You may be in a similar situation where there is no end in sight, hoping for even a momentary glimpse into the future. Who has never wished they knew what their future held? The mystery of tomorrow has captivated people since the beginning of time.

There are those who have the gift of intuition, who are good at predicting certain future events, but most of that is based on current realities. Nobody this side of heaven can predict the future with any degree of certainty, yet people keep trying.

Billions of dollars are spent each year on psychics, in the U. S. alone by people desperate to understand the future. It is an industry that shows growth during economic downturns. Our quest for knowledge and control leads us to believe that somehow if we know what is coming, we can be better prepared, or able to alter the course of events.

We can modify our behavior, or make decisions that can affect future events, but there is no possible way to predict the future. There are too many moving parts for which we have no control. Every day we come into contact with other people, whose actions, motives, and decisions have nothing to do with us. Your life is filled with actions and situations you cannot control.

If you have a loved one who is participating in self-destructive behavior, there is continuous anxiety over the future. Your loved one has repeatedly been lost. If you're experiencing a serious health issue, you will want to know if and when you will be healed.

You may have struggled to find a lasting relationship, or have been hurt and wonder when you will find true happiness with another person. Beasts can keep us in a constant state of panic and anxiety over the future.

Today is the only day you are guaranteed, so today should be the most important day of your life. We need to quit trying to figure out what is going to happen in the future. Instead, live in faith that you can handle whatever the future holds. Develop more peace, patience, and wisdom, so you will be more prepared for the future, and able to live fully in the present.

## Thank You Very Much

It is easy to be thankful when everything is going well. How thankful do you feel when all hell breaks loose? That is when your faith is put to the test. It is when you begin to understand that not all blessings come in the form of big bank accounts, great jobs, loving spouses, or perfect children.

There is always something for which to be thankful. Start with the fact you are breathing. Every day you are given the gift of life you should hit your knees and thank God. If you can't find something to be thankful for right now this very moment, then you're not looking very hard.

 **Stop right now and name something you're thankful for, and give God thanks for whatever came to your mind.**

 **Several times throughout each day, recognize your gifts and blessings and be grateful no matter how small they may seem at the time.**

Some of the most valuable blessings will come to you in the form of a roadblock, hurdle, or challenge, or in the form of a Beast. When all hell breaks loose, it can force you to your knees, or flat onto your face. The opportunity for spiritual growth is tremendous during times of trial. However, you may have to look harder to find it when your world seems to be falling apart.

When you can be thankful, not just in spite of your circumstances, but because of them, you will be far more thankful when things are going well.

When I started this exercise many years ago, I tried not to leave anything out. Each day I would come up with something new. There are some things that you should be thankful for, that you might not think about. We are often reluctant to admit that we are thankful for material things, but I certainly am thankful, for instance, for clothing and electricity! They may not be the most important, but let's be honest. There are many material things for which you are grateful to have.

This is not a contest to see who has the biggest list, but I do want you to consider as many aspects of your life in making your list. It is likely that you are thankful for more people, and things than you might have initially considered. Let me help you get thinking by showing you just a few from my huge list:

**I AM THANKFUL FOR:** ( a few of mine in no particular order)

| | |
|---|---|
| Sense of humor | Sean (son) |
| Rich (husband) | Food |
| God | Life lessons |
| The internet | Not giving up |
| Freedom | Running water |
| Ability to help others | Air travel |
| Shiska (my cat) | My family |

Now it is your turn. Jot down anything that comes to your mind, without concern for the order. If the order is important to you, you can go back and do that later. For now, let your mind and your heart flow. This is your personal list; you are not required to show it to anyone, so refrain from adding names or things that you think other people would expect you to include. Don't exclude things that you think others might not approve of having on your list. Revisit the list and add to it as you think of things.

**I AM THANKFUL FOR:**

| | |
|---|---|
| _____ | _____ |
| _____ | _____ |
| _____ | _____ |
| _____ | _____ |
| _____ | _____ |
| _____ | _____ |
| _____ | _____ |
| _____ | _____ |
| _____ | _____ |
| _____ | _____ |
| _____ | _____ |
| _____ | _____ |
| _____ | _____ |
| _____ | _____ |
| _____ | _____ |
| _____ | _____ |
| _____ | _____ |
| _____ | _____ |
| _____ | _____ |

I hope that eventually there will not be enough space to list all of the things for which you are thankful.

## Blessings and Miracles

*"There are only two ways to live your life. One is as though nothing is a miracle. The other is as though everything is a miracle."*

*— Albert Einstein*

I refer to the guy who shot Jordan in 2004 as, "The Guy." The bullet was lodged in Jordan's abdominal wall. The Guy pled guilty on a Wednesday, and on Sunday, Jordan called me and told me the bullet had come out of her body. I knew this defied logic, considering the location of the bullet. She said she had passed it during a bowel movement.

I had only been outside of the apartment where Jordan was living. It was in a small suburban town not exactly known for violence, but the building wasn't in a particularly nice part of that town. After she had been shot, I continued to fear something else could happen to her. I jumped to the conclusion the bullet she found in the toilet could not be hers, but that she was living in a place where bullets appeared in toilets!

Jordan insisted, "Mom, it's not a different bullet. It just came out when I went to the bathroom."

I called our doctor and explained the situation to him.

He said, "It's not possible. The bullet is lodged in her abdominal wall. There is no migration path between the bullet and the digestive tract. It would have to make a hole in her colon, in order for it to pass in her stool."

The doctor ordered an x-ray to prove the bullet was still there. Nobody was more surprised than he was to learn the bullet we had brought to his office was indeed the 9-mm bullet fired from The Guy's gun. He went on to explain that there was no medical explanation for this reality. He suggested we take the x-ray to the surgeon at Harborview, certain it would be written up in the medical journals as a medical miracle.

Have you ever prayed for a miracle? I have many times. We somehow have the notion that a big blessing comes with a big bang. It would be pretty cool if we were praying for a miracle, and suddenly a bolt of lightning came out of the sky, and a choir of angels began to sing. There were many times I secretly hoped God would grab me by the back of the shirt and pick me up off my knees.

Blessings are often subtle, and if you are not paying attention, you might miss the kindness of a stranger or the perfect words spoken by a friend at the precise moment you needed to hear them.

Since they can happen slowly over time, you are often left with the impression that the turn of events wasn't a miracle, but rather came as a result of luck or your actions.

When I was on my frantic quest for peace, my prayer wasn't answered immediately. One day, though, I realized that I felt different. Afraid to believe I had somehow received the blessing of peace, I discounted the feeling. Day after day, in spite of the circumstances, I began to feel more peaceful. In fact, the situation with Jordan had spiraled further downward, yet I remained more peaceful than I had in years. The miracle of peace allowed me to start finding myself again.

Albert Einstein said that there are two ways to live; one as if nothing is a miracle and the other as if everything is a miracle. What an amazing perspective. If you are waiting for jaw-dropping, angel singing, lightning-from-the-sky miracles, you may be waiting awhile. Don't miss the everyday miracles.

 **Have you ever experienced a miracle?**

 **What everyday occurrences or realities can you consider a miracle?**

**You previously created a list of what you are thankful for, and those should align with your blessings. So I won't ask you to list what your blessings are, but do take a minute to go back to your thankful list and realize just how blessed you are, even in the middle of your mess.**

## Fitting the Pieces Together

When you **Get On Your Spiritual Armor**, you will gain more strength than you will find on your own, or from other people. It just might be your Spiritual Armor that gives you the courage to **Decide to Stand Up and Fight.** When you are wearing your Spiritual Armor, you're far more equipped to **Change Your Attitude, Adjust Your Focus,** and **Stop Being a Control Freak.** Your faith will help you to forgive yourself and allow you to **Stand On Your Story**, rather than in it, and to **Make Meaning From the Madness** that is your story. Spiritual strength reminds you of the amazing gift of people and the necessity to **Build Your Circle of Strength**. It will help you give yourself permission to matter and to **Put On Your Oxygen Mask.**

## Your Declaration

Complete the Get On Your Spiritual Armor declaration below. Read it out loud as many times as you need in order to have it settle in and begin to take root.

---

### Get On Your Spiritual Armor Declaration

I, _____ am in a battle with a Beast. My Beast

is: _____

_____

Today, _____, 20_____ I declare that although my Beast may be

bigger than me, it is not bigger than God. Today, I am calling in my "Big Gun."

_____

Signed

---

## Faith in the Battle

*"In addition to all this, take up the shield of faith, with which you can extinguish all the flaming arrows of the evil one."* **Ephesians 6:16**

We all have faith in something whether we admit it or not. Sometimes it is our own abilities and resources, or it may be found in science or medicine. It might be faith in a belief system such as religion or even human nature. As Christians, our faith is in our living, resurrected Lord Jesus. We are told in Ephesians 1:19-20 that the same power that God used to raise Christ from the dead and seat him in heavenly places is at work in us! We have limitless power at our disposal; but if we only pay attention to our bodies and our minds yet ignore our spirits, we cannot tap into it. Because we believe in God and His power to carry us through any battle, we are at a huge advantage. We truly do not have to be afraid of the Big Beast or of our Beast because as Valerie wrote, "God is your Big Gun in the battle with your Beast."

In light of this truth, we can look at putting on our Spiritual Armor as God's way of equipping us for the battles he knew we would have to face while living on Planet Earth. How do we take up the shield of faith when we are afraid of the fiery darts the enemy is shooting at us? Do we even have faith if we do not feel it in our darkest and most overwhelming moments? I believe faith is a gift upon salvation. It is not something we receive more or less of depending on the situation. It is always within us because the Spirit of God lives in us. Fear, weariness, loneliness, and isolation can make us question if we have any faith left at all, but it's in there. We just need to learn how to access it.

**Look up the following scriptures and note what they say about faith.**

**Ephesians 2:8-9**

**Luke 17:5-6**

**2 Corinthians 5:7**

**Hebrews 11:1**

Fear is the opposite of faith, and it has controlled me most of my life in some form or another. As a little girl, I was scared when my dad would come home after a night of drinking because he was always angry and loud, which led to my parents arguing. I also worried about everything that could go wrong and what I could do to prevent it. Because my dad was a fireman, I worried he would die in a fire. I worried about the safety of my mother, brother, and sister. After all, it's normal for little girls to live in fear and worry all the time, right? Well, worry sure feels normal when your Beast enters your life as a child and remains there until it becomes a full-grown Control Freak Beast. That Beast managed to slip in unnoticed, like a comfortable pair of slippers, so it was natural when the Beasts of codependency and enabling decided to show up as well. After all, they were at the Control Freak Beast's beck and call, and their job was to make me believe that if only I was the *perfect* daughter, I could keep my dad from drinking. Likewise, if I was the *perfect* mom, I could keep my son from becoming an addict. While I probably did not believe that perfection was truly possible, with my over-weighted sense of responsibility, I did come very close to believing I should be able to prevent or fix just about anything or anyone, and I worried what would happen if I couldn't.

Fear is a very big Beast that manages to paralyze us and keep us from stepping out in faith. Valerie had us write down our fears no matter how rational or irrational they seemed. Like Valerie's fear of heights, I have a fear of tight places, such as getting into cramped elevators or having an MRI. While it may seem irrational, for me it is real. I have learned to take small practical steps to overcome the control it tries to have over me. For instance, practicing breathing techniques or focusing my attention on something positive helps minimize the anxiety I feel in those situations. By learning to face my fears in environments that I have control over, I can implement these strategies to strengthen my faith in situations I have absolutely no control over. Likewise, if we want to grow our spiritual faith, we need to take actions to put it into practice.

**Look up the following scriptures. What is necessary to grow our faith?**

**Romans 10:17**

**James 1:22**

**James 2:26**

I have read a few acronyms for the word Faith. Here is one of my favorites: Full Assurance In The Heart. We learn that we grow our spiritual faith by hearing, believing and doing what the word of God tells us to. Just like Valerie had to put herself up in a plane and climb out on that cliff to face her fear of heights, we also must face our fears when the Beast is riding our back and yelling at the top of his lungs. One of the most practical ways to grow our faith is by reading the bible, writing down encouraging verses and reciting them or even memorizing them. The word gets planted in us, and the Spirit of God brings it to our remembrance as we need it. Growing in faith does not mean just reading the bible and believing it though; it means stepping out in faith and acting on it. This is where the real challenge begins.

**Read Mark 5:24-34**

**How does this story of this woman speak to you in your current situation?**

**Do you believe she felt fear or faith as she reached out to touch Jesus?**

**Does this story encourage you to step out in faith in this current battle you are in?**

**If so, what actions will you take to overcome your Beast?**

When Jesus was ready to leave this earth to return to heaven, he knew that his followers would miss him. They had spent three years with the living God walking in their presence. He was their friend, their teacher, their provider, and their comforter. Before he ascended, he promised to not leave them alone, so He sent the Holy Spirit to be with them and remind them of everything He had taught them. He would be with them when they were scared, hurting, and lonely, and likewise, he is with us also.

*"But the Advocate, the Holy Spirit, whom the Father will send in my name, will teach you all things and will remind you of everything I have said to you."* **John 14:26**

**Look up the following scriptures and note what they say about the Word of God.**

**John 1:1**

**Isaiah 40:8**

**Hebrews 4:12**

**Do you believe that God is speaking to you personally through His word or does it at times feel cliché or for everyone else?**

 **Take a few minutes and pray, asking God to show you any past experiences or preconceived ideas you've established as a belief system that may have a negative impact on accepting the bible as active and personal in your situation. Note what they are and how they will need to change in order to grow your faith.**

Patience is a challenge for most people, although I have heard it said, "She has the patience of Job." Patience does not come naturally for this type A, take-charge personality. Perhaps, that is why my trials seem to take so long to cease, to give me a little extra practice. In my quest for peace, I now understand that without patience there is no peace. When my impatient mind yells and screams, "fix this and fix it now," patience takes a back seat and gives my Control Freak Beast the wheel. Once again, life doesn't feel in control at all. I no longer feel peaceful, but instead tired, overwhelmed, and anxious. I think most women can understand how subtly we slip from peace to panic within a few short minutes. I slip into hyperdrive; my mind starts racing, and I start obsessing over the situation and how I can fix it. My peace flies out the window as my Control Freak Beast goes speeding down the highway at full throttle.

One definite sign we have lost our peace is when we start to worry, and worry is often rooted in fear of the unknown. These fears, while sometimes substantiated, are usually irrational though because we can only speculate on the future and worry about what may or may not happen. Sometimes we worry because there is absolutely nothing else we feel we can do.

**Look up the following scriptures and write them out:**

**Philippians 4:6-7**

**Psalm 56:3-4**

**According to these passages, what do we have permission to worry or be fearful about?**

**How are we to combat fear, anxiety, and worry?**

Valerie encouraged us to cultivate an attitude of gratitude by listing people and things we are grateful for. One thing that I am truly thankful for during this time of hardship and the unknown is the faith God has given me. I do not know what I would do or where I would be without it. Yes, it is often tested in the fire, but the Lord has armed me with what I need to get through this battle and many others I might face. He gives us so many blessings to be thankful for. Thankfulness feeds our souls and strengthens our faith.

**Go back and review your gratitude list and see if there is anything or anyone else you would like to add to that list. You might just find there are a lot more people and things you can add to it.**

*"Life is a hard fight, a struggle, a wrestling with the principle of evil,*

*hand to hand, foot to foot. Every inch of the way is disputed."*

**Florence Nightingale**

## *Action # 3: Put On Your Oxygen Mask*

"Whether or not another person gives you permission or changes their own behavior, you <u>must</u> give yourself permission to put the pieces of your life back together."

— *Valerie Silveira*

## Action Introduction

If you have not given yourself permission to matter, it is likely that you are not taking good care of your physical, mental, or emotional health. Too often, we take care of everyone else, and everything else before we take the time to care for our own needs. Women are especially prone to taking a backseat in life. Mothers are cursed when it comes to even considering their own needs before their children, husbands, friends, and even the family dog! When you're having trouble putting yourself at the top, at least get your name on the list.

## Taking Care of You

*Stress*

In 1992, during a routine physical, my doctor noticed a lump on one of my thyroid glands. Reluctantly, I agreed to drink radioactive iodine out of a lead container. In the nuclear medicine department, they shut me alone in a room with a heavy door and instructed me to drink the liquid that would taste like stale water.

A couple of years later, after a quick ten-pound weight gain, and crawling up the stairs to my bed each day, I had another blood test. I was now hypothyroid; my thyroid was underactive, more like not functioning. Much to my disappointment, I would be on thyroid medication for life and strapped with a condition that affected my metabolism. Among other things, this would mean a negative impact on my weight and energy level.

For years, my weight and energy level were only slightly affected by my thyroid condition. After several years on the Roller Coaster From Hell, it changed. My brain became foggy, and I never felt rested, no matter how much sleep I managed to get. I began to gain weight no matter how I ate, or how much I exercised.

A few years ago, I was working with an internist who specializes in integrative medicine and age management. After extensive blood tests, the doctor sat with me to go over the results.

"Your adrenals are shot," she told me.

Nobody wants to hear from a medical professional that anything is "shot." I understood the basics of adrenal glands but had no idea how this condition would affect my life.

"Have you been through an extended period of stress?"

I believe I may have laughed when she asked that question. I then gave her a snapshot of the past few years. She nodded her head as if to say, "yes, that would do it."

Currently, I am dealing with some other health issues related to stress. There is no question living with a Beast has physically beaten me up. Eventually, your Beast will beat you up physically. Don't underestimate the impact stress can have on your body.

 **Have you experienced health issues that you believe are related to your high stress level?**

*Go Outside and Play*

Nature is a great healer. There is nothing like the solitude of an early morning walk where there is no sound but the birds, or the breeze through the trees. Not many things rival a mountain hike or a walk along a beach. Nature is an amazing setting to de-stress, think, or connect with your spirit.

A Time article in 2009 discussed "Eco-Therapy for Environmental Depression."[i]

> *"Depressed people often need someone to hug. On occasion, that someone may just be a tree. A new and growing group of psychologists believe that many of our modern-day mental problems, including depression, stress, and anxiety, can be*

*traced in part to society's increasing alienation from nature. The solution? Get outside and enjoy it. "*

Get into the outdoors. Spend time at a river, a lake, or at the ocean. Take a walk in the forest, or hike up a mountain trail. Take an early morning or evening walk around your neighborhood. Go hug a tree.

**Do you spend any significant amount of time outdoors?**

**What outdoor activities do you enjoy, or might you enjoy if you tried?**

### Work It, Baby, Work It!

My trips to the gym began in high school. It was how my friend Janet and I justified downing a plate of tortilla chips smothered in cheese afterward. In those days, I could have skipped the workout since plates of nachos didn't affect my weight one way or another. Since my metabolism button was turned off, I can't even look at a plate of chips piled with cheese without gaining weight. I'm extra motivated to exercise due to the metabolism issues.

You might not be too excited about exercising, but the benefits are worth it, and not so that you can eat a plate of nachos. Aside from the fitness benefit, it also helps to decrease stress and increase energy.

According to **WebMD.com**, people who regularly exercise benefit with a positive boost in mood and lower rates of depression:

### What Are the Psychological Benefits of Exercise With Depression? [ii]

*Improved self-esteem is a key psychological benefit of regular physical activity. When you exercise, your body releases chemicals called endorphins. These endorphins interact with the receptors in your brain that reduce your perception of pain.*

*Endorphins also trigger a positive feeling in the body, similar to that of morphine. For example, the feeling that follows a run or workout is often described as "euphoric." That feeling, known as a "runner's high," can be accompanied by a positive and energizing outlook on life.*

*Endorphins act as analgesics, which mean they diminish the perception of pain. They also act as sedatives. They are manufactured in your brain, spinal cord, and many other parts of your body and are released in response to brain chemicals called neurotransmitters. The neuron receptors endorphins bind to are the same ones that bind some pain medicines. However, unlike with morphine, the activation of these receptors by the body's endorphins does not lead to addiction or dependence.*

- *Regular exercise has been proven to:*
    - *Reduce stress*
    - *Ward off anxiety and feelings of depression*
    - *Boost self-esteem*
    - *Improve sleep*
- *Exercise also has these added health benefits:*
    - *It strengthens your heart.*
    - *It increases energy levels.*
    - *It lowers blood pressure.*
    - *It improves muscle tone and strength.*

o   *It strengthens and builds bones.*

o   *It helps reduce body fat.*

o   *It makes you look fit and healthy.*

### Is Exercise a Treatment for Clinical Depression?

*Research has shown that exercise is an effective but often underused treatment*

*for mild to moderate depression.*

Not only is exercise good for your physical health, but the endorphins released act as your natural happy pill!

If you're suffering from clinical depression, you should seek the advice of a professional, but don't ignore the physical, emotional, and psychological benefits of exercise. There are way too many options these days to have any real excuse for not exercising, assuming you are physically capable.

 **What is your current exercise routine & how often do you do it?**

 **If you are not exercising three or four times a week, what is keeping you from doing so?**

### When the Sun Goes Down

My cat stays on the bed at night, but he doesn't sleep much. Shiska waits for the slightest movement as an indication; it's time for the three of us to get up. He goes through periods where he doesn't bother waiting; instead, he sits next to the bed and meows just loud enough to wake me.

Like Shiska, the Beast is wide-awake at night, waiting for any chance to wake you from a restful sleep. He takes the opportunity the darkness of night provides, to increase your fear. When you are awake in the night, your already overstressed brain may go into overdrive, making it nearly impossible to fall back to sleep. You will toss and turn, unable to shut down your thoughts.

If sleep does come, when you awake, you feel no more rested than when you went to bed. This continuous cycle and your body's inability to rejuvenate will make it harder for you to see the light at the end of the tunnel.

Sleep is critical for healing and energizing the body, mind, and soul. There are numerous methods people use successfully to get a good night's sleep. Some of them are:

- Prayer
- Meditation
- Yoga
- Hot bath
- Tea
- Warm milk
- Hot shower
- Essential oils
- Removing all electronic devices from the bedroom
- Sleep mask
- Sound machine
- Earplugs
- Counting sheep (that didn't work for me - I once counted to five thousand!)
- Sleep medication

Work to find something you can do to get a good night's sleep. If lack of sleep has become a serious problem, you may want to consider seeking medical attention.

 **Physical Well-Being**

**List the top three ways in which your physical health is affecting the quality of your life. In the space just to the right of each, write down one small step that you can take TODAY to improve the situation.**

1. _____     _____

2. _____     _____

3. _____     _____

 **Mental Well-Being**

**List the top three ways in which your Mental health is affecting the quality of your life. In the space just to the right of each, write down one small step that you can take TODAY to improve the situation.**

1. _____     _____

2. _____     _____

3. _____     _____

**Emotional Well-Being**

**List the top three ways in which your Emotional health is affecting the quality of your life. In the space just to the right of each, write down one small step that you can take TODAY to improve the situation.**

1. _____      _____

2. _____      _____

3. _____      _____

**Note: for any serious physical, mental, or emotional health condition, consult a health professional.**

## Laughter is the Best Medicine

Not many people would argue the benefits of laughter, but did you know studies have proven the psychological, mental, and even physical benefits of laughter?

The Mayo Clinic published an article stating that a good laugh has more benefits than lightening your load mentally. They explained that laughing actually induces physical changes in your body and can: stimulate many organs, activate and relieve stress response, soothe tension, improve your immune system, relieve pain, increase personal satisfaction, and improve your mood. [iii]

The sitcom, "Seinfeld" that ran from 1989 to 1998, and is still shown in syndication is a great example of *everyday life humor*. It has been referred to as, a *show about nothing,* but in reality, it was a show about everything. Each episode dealt with a subject or several subjects that were relatable. It allowed us to laugh at the characters, and at ourselves. Finding the humor in everyday life will lighten the load you're carrying. We need to be more serious about not being so serious.

 **Do you try to find humor in everyday life?**

One morning, years ago, I stood in a circle chatting with a few coworkers before the workday began. The Wonder Bra, with its small removable bra pads, had hit the United States.

As I talked with my coworkers, I noticed one of my bra pads had escaped and was lying on the floor near my foot. Glancing around the circle, it appeared nobody else had noticed, so I carefully slid my foot over and stepped on the bra pad.

As the conversation began to wind down, it would have been natural for me to excuse myself and head to my office, but I stood frozen unable to move without revealing my secret. I waited awkwardly until the last person walked away, before bending down and scooping up the bra pad. I retreated to my office, closed the door, and laughed my head off. Of course, I couldn't wait to retell the story.

When my grandfather died, my mother and I were at the funeral home, wrapping up the preparations for the memorial service. The funeral director was finishing some paperwork and suggested we go take a look at the chapel where the service would be held.

His directions led us down a long hallway, lined with doors. We were in conversation and not paying much attention to the doors. As we passed one of them, we couldn't help but notice a woman standing over a body. My mom was startled and let out a gasp, causing the woman to look up from the body as we passed by the open door.

The situation seemed very funny to me, but I didn't want to offend the woman as I was uncertain as to whether or not she was a family member or simply worked at the funeral home.

Stifling my laughter, I took off at a dead run toward the chapel, with mom following. We burst through the doors and fell onto a pew, laughing hysterically. No doubt, my Scottish grandfather with his whacky sense of humor was lying across his pew in heaven, laughing with us.

We should laugh every chance we get. If you're not prone to laughter, get around some funny people or watch a funny television show or a comedic movie. Find humor in everyday life. As long as you're not laughing at other people, do whatever it is that makes you laugh; it's a free prescription for good mental and physical health.

 **Complete the blanks below and score yourself on the Humor Meter.**

**Section 1: Next to each question, enter the appropriate number: 0) I don't remember; 1) At least a week ago; 2) This week; 3) today.**

_____When was the last time you genuinely smiled?

_____When was the last time you laughed when you were alone?

_____When was the last time that you laughed?

_____When was the last time that you laughed and could not stop?

_____When was the last time you made someone else laugh?

\_\_\_\_\_Section TOTAL

**Section 2: Next to each question, enter the appropriate number: 0) Never; 1) Sometimes; 2) Most of the time; 3) Always**

_____I have no problem being the first to laugh at a situation.

_____I cannot imagine life without a lot of laughter.

_____I don't wait for someone to smile at me before I smile at them.

_____I laugh when I am alone.

_____I believe that laughter has a positive impact on my health.

_____Section TOTAL

**Section 3:** Next to each question, enter the appropriate number: 0) Not so much; 1) I can go either way; 2) True; 3) Absolutely

_____I love to laugh.

_____I find humor in everyday life.

_____Laughter is very important to me.

_____I tend to laugh when I hear the laughter of others.

_____I like making others laugh.

_____ Section TOTAL

**Section 4:** Next to each question, enter the appropriate number: 0) No way; 1) Yes, but I would never admit it; 2) Yes; 3) For sure

_____I have laughed in a situation that others might find inappropriate.

_____I have started to laugh and had a hard time stopping.

_____I sometimes laugh so hard that my cheeks or my stomach hurt.

_____I would like to laugh that hard every single day.

_____Often, I amuse myself with humor & if someone else finds it funny, it's a bonus.

_____TOTAL

_____GRAND TOTAL - ALL SECTIONS

**Find your score on the Humor meter below:**

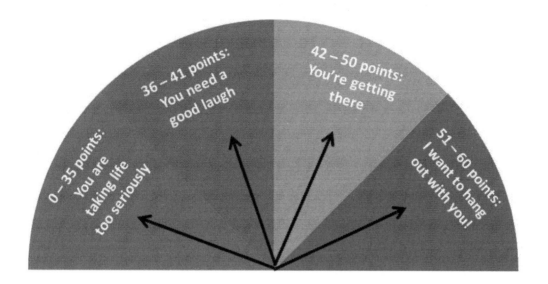

## Codependency and You

Codependency is a common word in the world of alcohol or drug addiction. The term was originally used to describe people who were in a relationship with a chemically dependent person.

One definition of codependency is: "A codependent person is one who has let another person's behavior affect him or her, and who is obsessed with controlling that person's behavior."

The term codependency wasn't new to me, having heard it used over the years in reference mainly to spouses of alcoholics. I didn't pay much attention to the term I would one-day use in describing myself.

For me, it happened gradually, and by the time I realized what was happening, I was living as a codependent. In looking through definitions and lists of behaviors, I can see now that I have a tendency toward certain codependent behaviors. It's natural for me to put the interests or well-being of others before my own. Had Jordan not become addicted to drugs, though, I might not have recognized myself as having a "mild case" of codependency.

A young woman in recovery said to me recently, "You're the worst kind of person to be the mother of an addict since you are so generous and put others first. An addict will eat you alive."

It can be uncomfortable for some of us to admit, even to ourselves, that we have codependent tendencies, or that we are demonstrating serious codependent behavior. The codependency label didn't sit very well with me since it flies in the face of my independent and confident nature, but when Jordan went sideways, my codependent tendencies surfaced.

If the actions and behaviors of your loved one are causing you to lose your identity or to obsess over that person's life, you are in danger. Codependency is like a thief, robbing you of your perspective, independence, and self-love. Had I not found a way to manage my codependency, I was in danger of completely losing me, and anyone else I cared about.

 **Are you in danger of losing yourself in the actions and behaviors of another person?**

 **Take a look at the questions below. Circle any that you can relate to. If you can identify with several symptoms, you may be codependent.**

1. Do you keep quiet to avoid arguments?

2. Are you always worried about others' opinions of you?

3. Have you ever lived with someone with an alcohol or drug problem?

4. Have you ever lived with someone who hits or belittles you?

5. Are the opinions of others more important than your own?

6. Do you have difficulty adjusting to changes at work or home?

7. Do you feel rejected when significant others spend time with friends?

8. Do you doubt your ability to be who you want to be?

9. Are you uncomfortable expressing your true feelings to others?

10. Have you ever felt inadequate?

11. Do you feel like a "bad person" when you make a mistake?

12. Do you have difficulty taking compliments or gifts?

13. Do you feel humiliation when your child or spouse makes a mistake?

14. Do you think people in your life would go downhill without your constant efforts?

15. Do you frequently wish someone could help you get things done?

16. Do you have difficulty talking to people in authority, such as the police or your boss?

17. Are you confused about who you are or where you are going with your life?

18. Do you have trouble saying "no" when asked for help?

19. Do you have trouble asking for help?

20. Do you have so many things going at once that you can't do justice to any of them?

## Who Is Wearing Your Oxygen Mask?

If you have traveled by air more than a handful of times, you pay very little attention to the flight attendants as they go through the pre-flight safety demonstration. Next time you are on an airplane and the flight attendants begin the process, look around at the other passengers and see what they are doing. You will see people talking, reading, staring out the window, or already in dreamland. Now and then, you may notice a passenger or two listening and watching intently as the flight attendant goes through the drill; they are probably infrequent air travelers. Those of us who have been on hundreds of flights could recite the pre-flight instructions in our sleep.

One important part of the demonstration is the explanation of the oxygen mask. We are told in the case of a loss in cabin pressure, that an oxygen mask will be released from overhead. Instructions are given as to how to properly place the oxygen mask on your face and exactly how the mask will react as you begin to breathe.

You are further instructed to **put the oxygen mask on your own face before trying to assist others around you.** If you pass out, you will not be able to help anyone around you.

Who Is Wearing Your Oxygen Mask? Think carefully about this. Yes, we should give some of our oxygen to others. Sure, we should allow others to lean on us from time to time. That is the beautiful thing about human relationships. The trouble begins when you are putting all of your energy into another person, at the expense of taking care of yourself.

If you don't have anyone in your life who encourages you to take care of yourself, then you might reconsider those relationships. It is likely that you have at least one person who has tried to encourage you to give yourself permission to be happy; to matter.

**List the people who have encouraged you to be happy; to take care of yourself. These are the people who are NOT wearing your oxygen mask:**

- _____

- _____

- _____

- _____

- _____

**List the people in your life who might be taking up too much of your oxygen and explain why you are allowing the situation to continue.**

- _____

- _____

- _____

- _____

- _____

## Being Okay with Being Okay

I love traveling; meeting new people and experiencing different cultures and customs. There is one trip I have taken extensively - the guilt trip. You may have taken a few of these trips yourself.

If your Beast is tied to another person's behavior, then you struggle with whether or not it's okay for you to be okay when your loved one isn't.

As the mother of an addict, I lived with the constant guilt over enjoying life while my daughter was poisoning her body. It didn't feel right for me to feel peaceful while Jordan was lost. I would begin to enjoy myself, only to allow an overwhelming feeling of guilt to wash over me, ruining the moment or the entire day. As a mother, how was I to leave my only daughter behind while I moved on with my life?

Annette's first marriage was to a man who was a raging alcoholic. He became infuriated when Annette paid bills with his drinking money. Although she loved him, Annette was at the end of her rope. She called Tom's mother and was surprised by her response.

"You need to step over him," Tom's mother told her.

She was a recovered alcoholic and knew firsthand that Tom was holding Annette back. It was the mother's *permission* that allowed Annette to *step over* Tom and move on with her life. Years later, Tom called Annette to make amends.

It was the mother's choice of words that likely saved Annette from many more years of anguish. She didn't suggest Annette leave Tom or walk away from him. She told Annette to "step over him." In other words, it was Tom's choice to stay where he was, but Annette was not required to stay there, drowning with him. She could keep moving, stepping over him, on her way.

Tom's mother told Annette it was okay for her to be okay, even though her own son wasn't. It was a selfless thing for a mother to do, and she was able to do it because she understood that only Tom could save Tom.

Just because someone else is choosing not to be okay, it is still okay for you to be okay. In fact, choose to be better than okay.

 **Are you feeling guilty about getting on with your own life while someone you care about is stuck where they are?**

## Give Yourself Permission to Matter

Others can try to convince you that you matter, but until you give yourself permission, nothing will change. Rich tried to get me to focus on myself over Jordan for years. Friends encouraged me to do the same. Certain family members voiced concern about my mental, physical, and emotional health. People who had walked the codependency path advised me that it was time for me to help myself. They all gave me permission to matter, but it wasn't until I gave myself permission, that I began to matter to me.

You may or may not have people in your life who encourage you to take care of yourself. If you're an approval seeker, your natural tendency will be to wait for the approval of others. In either case, you could be waiting awhile. Ultimately, you have to be both the permission giver and the permission receiver.

Logically, Jordan is the last person from whom I should need permission to take care of myself. For some reason, there was a long period when I was waiting for permission from her. The drug Beast is selfish and self-centered and would never have given me the permission.

Whether or not another person gives you permission or changes their behavior, you must give yourself permission to put the pieces of your life back together.

**List all of the reasons (excuses) that you have used, or are currently using for NOT giving yourself permission to matter.**

- _____

- _____

- _____

- _____

- _____

- _____

- _____

- _____

Take some time to review the reasons that you listed above. Step back for a moment and think about what you might tell a friend who gave you all of the same reasons. Would you tell your friend that many of the reasons they listed, were really excuses? Often our reasons are masked in humility, in caring more for others than for ourselves, so it is easy to think of them as valid reasons. The bottom line is that you must take care of yourself, or you are going to go down in flames. There will be nothing left of you to care for anyone else.

### Fitting the Pieces Together

When you **Put On Your Oxygen Mask**, you will have more energy and stamina for battle. Giving yourself permission to matter will ensure that each time that you are knocked down, you will **Decide to Stand Up and Fight**, one more time. Self-love will give you more reason to **Change Your Attitude, Adjust Your Focus and** to **Stop Being a Control Freak.** Self-care inspires you to **Stand <u>On</u> Your Story.** Believing in yourself is essential for believing you can **Make Meaning From the Madness.** Loving yourself will allow you to love others and to **Build Your Circle of Strength.** Realizing you matter to God will propel you to **Get On Your Spiritual Armor**.

You do not need permission from me or anyone else. In case it's the nudge you need, I hereby give you permission to matter. Now give it to yourself.

## Your Declaration

Fill in the blanks of the Put On Your Oxygen Mask declaration, giving yourself permission to matter. It is your resolve to put your oxygen mask on your own face before attempting to assist others.

---

### Put On Your Oxygen Mask Declaration

I, _____ am in a battle with a Beast.

My Beast is: _____

_____

Today, _____, 20_____ I hereby give myself permission to matter. I declare that I am valuable and understand that unless I put the Oxygen Mask on my own face first, I will not have the energy for anyone else. Taking care of me IS taking care of others.

_____
Signed

---

## Faith in the Battle

*"Dear friend, I pray that you may enjoy good health and that all may go well with you, even as your soul is getting along well."*

**3 John 1: 2**

I have a new appreciation for the saying, "put your own oxygen mask on your face before trying to assist others around you." I will never forget the feeling of suffocating and the fear I felt not being able to expand my lungs and breathe in freely. My head hurt, my chest hurt, and I was exhausted beyond explanation. I knew something was seriously wrong and heard the Lord speak to my heart, "Go to your doctor and tell her something is very wrong and if she doesn't find it, you will die." For weeks, I had been slowly deteriorating. I was still working and trying to function, but the progressively increasing pressure in my chest and inability to walk and talk at the same time eventually became something I could no longer ignore. I was fairly young and in excellent health, so the last thing I would suspect was that later that day I would be hospitalized with a life-threatening pulmonary embolism. The oxygen I so longed for I struggled to receive. The hospital provided me with the oxygen I needed to save my life and the medications necessary to break up the blood clot and restore me back to health. As a child, I suffered from severe asthma and remember the fearful days separated from my family by the plastic sheets of the oxygen tent. Today, I cherish my ability to breathe without obstruction. I appreciate fresh air more than you can imagine, so when Valerie called us to Action 3, Put On Your Oxygen Mask, I literally knew what she meant. When the Lord sounded the alarm to me to go and get help, or I would die, I stopped denying how seriously sick I really was and finally took action! Our Beasts are choking the life out of us, and we have been surviving by holding our breath and putting our oxygen masks on others we felt needed more than we did. It's time to put on our own life-saving oxygen masks and breathe in deeply.

*"The Spirit of God has made me; the breath of the Almighty gives me life."*

**Job 33:4**

"He may be your baby, but you're my baby, and I worry about you." I'll never forget my mother's emotion-filled words as I shared with her the story of yet another encounter with my son's addiction Beast. She loves her grandson beyond measure, but in truth, she loves me more. I am her daughter, her little girl, and I will always be so no matter how old I grow. As we grow into adulthood, we may begin to identify ourselves with certain labels such as so-and-so's wife or mother, sister or daughter. It is easy to forget who we were before we stepped into our present role. Think back to before you were a wife, a mother, or an employee. You were someone's child. Someone loved you and cared for you. That, someone, was God, and He loves you very much. Tear off the labels your Beast wants to put on you and wear the only one that is true, Child of the King!

*"For you are all children of God through faith in Christ Jesus."* - **Galatians 3:26**

As Valerie wrote earlier, because we are body, mind & spirit, it is important that we do not neglect ourselves in the areas of our health and well-being. When I had my "Aha" moment, I realized that even though I was going through the motions of taking care of myself, they had become mechanical and ineffective. I was praying, reading the Bible, trying to eat right, and exercising so I could check them off my "to-do" list, but inside I was sick from fear and worry. I would lay awake at night with my heart and mind racing, unable to rest. I was fixated on fixing my son and controlling his addiction Beast. While I prayed, my unfocused mind obsessed over what I needed God to do to repair our tormented lives. During work, I found my mind wandering away from conversations that needed my full attention. I felt exhausted and could barely make it through a class at the gym. Sadly, even the dinner hour became a source of tears as I pleaded with my husband to come up with a solution to the mess our lives had become. I had become a shell of the person I used to be as the role of an "addict's mom" took over every facet of my life. Worse yet, it left the other members of my family feeling forgotten and probably unloved. Putting on our oxygen masks is necessary not only for ourselves but for the sake of all our other important relationships as well.

 **Look up the following scriptures and write them out.**

**Matthew 11:28**

**Psalm 94:19**

**Isaiah 40:29**

**In what ways do these verses show God's concern for our health and well-being?**

**What are we instructed to do to get and maintain good emotional and physical health?**

Stress has an eerie way of affecting everything in our lives. Like a cancer creeping in unannounced, it takes over every fiber of our being often before we become aware of its presence. There are so many practical ways to de-stress, and one of the best ways is to learn to give our biggest burdens and deepest fears to God. Earlier we read that Jesus wants us to come to him when we are tired and burnt out. The verse continues…" Take my yoke upon you. Let me teach you because I am humble and gentle at heart, and you will find rest for your souls. For my yoke is easy to bear, and the burden I give you is light." **Matthew 11:29-30.** Learning to give our problems to the Lord is often easier said than done. Let's start by acknowledging our burdens and the effect carrying them has on us.

 **List the heavy burdens you are carrying at this time.**

 **What effect are they having on you physically, emotionally, mentally and spiritually?**

**What would it feel like to be free from that burden if you were able to let the Lord carry for you?**

It is hard to feel joy when our children or other loved ones are suffering. I can remember telling our family's substance abuse counselor once that I would never be happy again. His silent stare told me if that was the case, then I had better do something about it right away! As I heard myself say those hopeless words, I could not believe that they were coming out of my mouth. Valerie shared the definition of codependency earlier as "one who has let another person's behavior affect him or her, and who is obsessed with controlling that person's behavior." The church has been reluctant to label people as being codependent, perhaps because it is not mentioned verbatim in the bible. This may not sound like you, but if those words I spoke to my counselor do not sound like they were spoken by a codependent, I don't know what is.

Stress has an incredible way of stealing everything from us, though, and sadly I meant every word I said, at least in that moment. What changed for me? I finally realized that my life was a gift from God. He had called me to live it fully and joyfully. He knew that in my own strength that would be impossible. He knew the battles I had to face would leave me wounded and barren IF I fought them on my own. Wisely, he let me carry the weight of the whole world on my shoulders until I was too exhausted to take another step without asking for his help. The journey back to joy came with a lot of bumps in the road. I, like most women, have a hard time keeping my mind off my problems. We lose our focus, and it takes practice to get back into a more positive mindset. Giving ourselves permission to matter means allowing uninterrupted time to be refreshed and renewed in the Lord's presence and enjoying time with our husbands, children, and dear friends. It means saying it's okay to laugh again at funny jokes or go to a movie or dinner out.  Putting on our own oxygen masks means giving ourselves permission to matter again. It is my prayer that you will be reminded today that you are someone's little girl and you are precious to Him. Put on your oxygen mask and celebrate!

**Look up these scriptures and write them out. Consider writing them on index cards and committing them to memory.**

**Nehemiah 8:10**

**Job 8:21**

**Isaiah 55:12**

*"Live by faith. Live out loud. And never stop believing God-day by day."*
**Beth Moore**

## *Action #4: Build Your Circle of Strength*

*"Lean on me, when you're not strong. And I'll be your friend; I'll help you carry on. For it won't be long til I'm gonna need, somebody to lean on."*

**— "Lean on Me," Bill Withers**

## Action Introduction

The more out of control Jordan's life became, the more I began to retreat. My comfort zone is being there for others; being strong at all times. While I clung to my so-called emotional strength, I was becoming weaker by the day. I preferred hiding in the walk-in closet crying, to being vulnerable enough to allow the people who care about me, to care for me.

We all need someone to lean on, to love, to learn from, to lead, and to follow. You may have your Spiritual Armor strapped on, but you will still need your Circle of Strength. Don't step onto the battlefield alone.

## The Circle of Strength

Although each journey is unique and personal, they are intertwined with the journeys of others. The Circle of Strength represents your people. There are four distinct groups in the Circle of Strength.

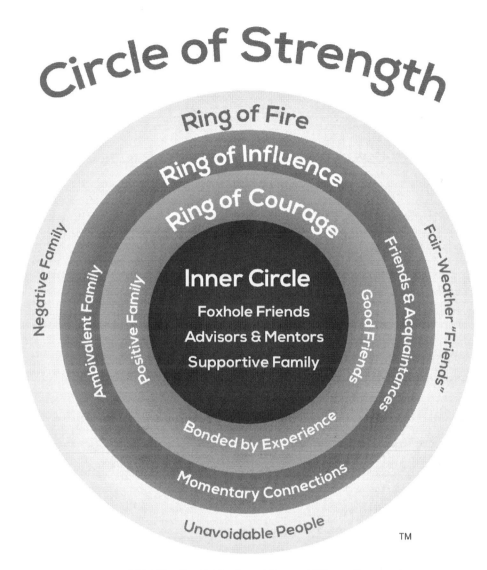

# Circle of Strength

Ring of Fire

Ring of Influence

Ring of Courage

**Inner Circle**

**Foxhole Friends**

**Advisors & Mentors**

**Supportive Family**

Negative Family

Ambivalent Family

Positive Family

Good Friends

Friends & Acquaintances

Fair-Weather "Friends"

Bonded by Experience

Momentary Connections

Unavoidable People

TM

### Inner Circle

At the core of the Circle of Strength is the Inner Circle. This group of people includes your foxhole friends, trusted advisors and mentors, supportive family, and possibly your spouse or partner.

Ideally, you should spend the greatest amount of time with those people in your Inner Circle; however, circumstances may prevent you from doing so. Despite the amount of time you can spend with the people in your Inner Circle, be certain you are most influenced by them. These are the relationships that will give you the most courage, strength, wisdom, knowledge, and comfort necessary for you to stand strong in your battle. These are the people that will battle with you.

### *Foxhole Friends*

A foxhole is "a small pit, usually for one or two soldiers dug as a shelter in a battle area."[iv] A foxhole friend will be at your side during the battle; next to you in the foxhole, and on the battlefield with you. Not only will a foxhole friend fight alongside you, but they would be willing to go out onto the battlefield and drag you back into the foxhole. Much is asked of a foxhole friend so they will be few and far between, but worth their weight in gold.

If you don't have at least one foxhole friend, work on developing a relationship to the point of having one. The best way to gain a foxhole friend is to be one.

 **Do you have at least one Foxhole Friend? If so, who is it?**

 **Why do you consider this person a Foxhole Friend?**

 **Are you the same kind of friend to your Foxhole Friend?**

**If you don't have a Foxhole Friend, what could you do in order to develop a relationship with someone in order to gain and to be, a Foxhole Friend?**

### Trusted Advisors and Mentors

You might automatically assume your Inner Circle will be comprised solely of your family and friends, but some of the most valuable people in your Inner Circle might be trusted advisors or mentors.

Often, we confide in spiritual leaders, counselors, life coaches, or mentors more than we do with others in our Inner Circle. You may feel more secure sharing your innermost feelings with one of these advisors or mentors, and can gain insight from them that others close to you are unable to provide.

 **Do you have advisors, mentors, teachers, pastors, spiritual teachers, counselors, or coaches in your Inner Circle? Who are they and why do you consider them part of your Inner Circle?**

### Family Members Who Support You Unconditionally

The bond family members have with one another can be some of the strongest bonds imaginable, or the most challenging. All of your family members will not be in the Inner

Circle. Since we all crave the approval of our families, it can be devastating when those you were certain would be the most supportive, end up letting you down. I am not suggesting you start cutting ties with family members unless they are abusive or antagonistic. We simply need to have realistic expectations when it comes to family or anyone else.

During my darkest days, I received some strong support from a few of my family members. I hope that there will be members of your family who are a part of your Inner Circle, but it is not necessary to include everyone simply because they are your family by blood, or by marriage.

 **Which of your family members support you unconditionally and how do they support you?**

 **Do you support these family members unconditionally? If so, how?**

### Spouse or Partner

It would stand to reason your spouse or partner would be part of your Inner Circle simply by virtue of your relationship. Based on what the Inner Circle represents, they may not fit. They may even be preventing you from standing up.

If your spouse or partner is not part of your Inner Circle, you need to determine why. I am certainly not advocating divorce or the ending of relationships. However, there are situations in which the very relationships that should make us better are destroying us. If that is the case, you should take a long hard look at your relationship, and take action to change the dynamics of that relationship. Life is short, and getting shorter every day.

 **Is your spouse or partner in your Inner Circle? Why, or why not?**

 **Do you expect the right amount of support from them; not more than you know they are capable of offering?**

 **If your expectations of your spouse are unreasonable, what ways could you change your attitude or expectations in order to avoid disappointment and frustration for both of you?**

The right people in your Inner Circle will fight with you, and for you. On those days when you don't have the strength to fight, it is okay to lie down. Let your circle fight for you. Then stand up again.

**Check off the characteristics a person would need to possess for you to consider them a part of your Inner Circle:**

- ❑ Accountable
- ❑ Authentic
- ❑ Calm
- ❑ Capable
- ❑ Compassionate
- ❑ Considerate
- ❑ Courageous
- ❑ Dependable
- ❑ Disciplined
- ❑ Empathetic
- ❑ Ethical
- ❑ Expressive
- ❑ Fair
- ❑ Faithful
- ❑ Fearless
- ❑ Generous
- ❑ Happy
- ❑ Honest
- ❑ Honorable
- ❑ Humble
- ❑ Independent
- ❑ Integrity
- ❑ Intelligent
- ❑ Listener
- ❑ Logical
- ❑ Loving
- ❑ Loyal
- ❑ Nurturing
- ❑ Open-Minded
- ❑ Optimistic
- ❑ Patient
- ❑ Peaceful
- ❑ Polite
- ❑ Punctual
- ❑ Responsible
- ❑ Sense of Humor
- ❑ Sincere
- ❑ Strong
- ❑ Supportive
- ❑ Trustworthy
- ❑ Truthful
- ❑ Wise

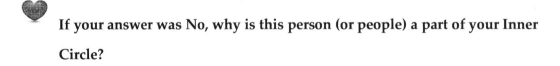

**Go back and look at the different people that you listed as part of your Inner Circle (Foxhole Friends, Trusted Advisors and Mentors, Family Members who support you unconditionally, and your Spouse or Partner). Do those people have most of the characteristics that you checked?**

**If your answer was No, why is this person (or people) a part of your Inner Circle?**

# Ring of Courage

The first ring surrounding the Inner Circle is the Ring of Courage. It is comprised of good friends, positive family members, and people who are bonded to you by a common experience.

## *Good Friends*

Mom always said you could count your true friends on one hand. Those true friends are your foxhole friends that reside in your Inner Circle. Beyond your foxhole friends, and far greater in numbers than foxhole friends, are your good friends. You can share most of your thoughts and feelings with them. Good friends may not drag you off the battlefield, but they just might be in the foxhole with you. For sure, they will be there for you most of the time.

 **List your good friends:**

## *Positive Family*

While a few of your family members may support you unconditionally, others will simply be a positive influence. They love you and will express genuine concern.

They are not in your Inner Circle. Yet, the mere fact they are positive is incredibly valuable. Be thankful they are in your corner, cheering you on.

**List your family members who may not support you unconditionally, but have a positive influence on you:**

### Bonded By Experience

Along the way, you will meet people who are on or have been on, a similar path as yours. With some of these people, you will develop an instantaneous bond.

As close as family and friends may be, most of them have not walked in your shoes. They may be empathetic, sympathetic, loving, and supportive, but unless they have been where you are, it is difficult for them to relate. A unique bond exists among those who have shared similar challenges and heartbreak.

There are many support groups people join for this very reason. The bond of life experience can be very strong. Find some people you can bond with over your common experience. A few may even end up in your Inner Circle.

Be careful, however, you don't wind up adding more stress to your battle. Many people have no real interest in battling their Beast. They have begun to identify themselves with their pain. We all know that misery loves company. Make sure people you bond with because of common experience are also standing up to their Beast, and not simply trying to suck you into living with theirs.

Do you have people in your Ring of Courage that you have bonded with because of your common experience? List their names:

Check off the characteristics a person would need to possess for you to consider them a part of your Ring of Courage:

| | | |
|---|---|---|
| ❑ Accountable | ❑ Fearless | ❑ Open-Minded |
| ❑ Authentic | ❑ Generous | ❑ Optimistic |
| ❑ Calm | ❑ Happy | ❑ Patient |
| ❑ Capable | ❑ Honest | ❑ Peaceful |
| ❑ Compassionate | ❑ Honorable | ❑ Polite |
| ❑ Considerate | ❑ Humble | ❑ Punctual |
| ❑ Courageous | ❑ Independent | ❑ Responsible |
| ❑ Dependable | ❑ Integrity | ❑ Sense of Humor |
| ❑ Disciplined | ❑ Intelligent | ❑ Sincere |
| ❑ Empathetic | ❑ Listener | ❑ Strong |
| ❑ Ethical | ❑ Logical | ❑ Supportive |
| ❑ Expressive | ❑ Loving | ❑ Trustworthy |
| ❑ Fair | ❑ Loyal | ❑ Truthful |
| ❑ Faithful | ❑ Nurturing | ❑ Wise |

Go back and look at the different people that you listed as part of your Ring of Courage. Do those people have most of the characteristics that you checked?

**If your answer was No, why do you consider this person in your Ring of Courage?**

## Ring of Influence

In your Ring of Influence are your friends and acquaintances, ambivalent or non-supportive family and people with whom you have momentary connections.

### Friends and Acquaintances

Most of the people we refer to as "friends" may actually be acquaintances. Call them what you want, these relationships do have a positive influence on us and our battle. If nothing else, these types of friends can distract you from your troubles for an evening.

They don't know you as well as your good friends and may not ask much about your situation, which can often be a big relief. There were many occasions when I was down, and Rich drug me to a social event with friends or acquaintances, or to meet new people. Often, I didn't want to go, and I made excuses not to attend once in a while. Most of the time, I went for Rich's sake, but every time came away thankful I had gone.

People in this group can be a source for new perspectives on your situation. Since they are not as intimate with your life or your battle, they are sometimes able to give insight that others closer to you are unable to provide.

You need an occasional break from your troubles, and even from the battle. People in your friends and acquaintances group can provide you with a much-needed distraction or break.

**Who are the Friends (Acquaintances) that are a source of fresh perspective and insight, or simply a distraction from your battle?**

Since these are not people that you are most influenced by, it may not be important to you that they have some of the characteristics of those in your Inner Circle and Ring of Courage. It is important to understand the roles that different people play in your life, so as to not place unrealistic expectations on people, and to set yourself up for disappointment.

**Check off the characteristics that would be important that the people who are Friends and Acquaintances possess, in order for them to be considered a positive influence in your life:**

| | | |
|---|---|---|
| ❏ Authentic | ❏ Generous | ❏ Open-Minded |
| ❏ Calm | ❏ Happy | ❏ Optimistic |
| ❏ Compassionate | ❏ Honest | ❏ Outgoing |
| ❏ Considerate | ❏ Honorable | ❏ Patient |
| ❏ Courageous | ❏ Humble | ❏ Peaceful |
| ❏ Dependable | ❏ Independent | ❏ Polite |
| ❏ Empathetic | ❏ Integrity | ❏ Punctual |
| ❏ Ethical | ❏ Intelligent | ❏ Sense of Humor |
| ❏ Expressive | ❏ Interesting | ❏ Sincere |
| ❏ Fair | ❏ Listener | ❏ Supportive |
| ❏ Faithful | ❏ Logical | ❏ Trustworthy |
| ❏ Fearless | ❏ Loving | ❏ Truthful |
| ❏ Fun | ❏ Nurturing | ❏ Wise |

**Do the people that you listed as Friends & Acquaintances possess most of the characteristics that you have checked off on the list?**

### Ambivalent or Non-Supportive Family

Members of families can be the best of friends and the most supportive and encouraging. They can also be some of the most negative, unsupportive, ambivalent people you will come across.

There is a sense of obligation and duty to stand beside family, and, therefore, some of the so-called support we receive from family isn't genuine.

Don't assume they don't care, as people react to situations in different ways. It could be that you have always been strong, so they are not used to offering support, or perhaps they are unsure how to help or what to say. Some family members are simply selfish or self-absorbed.

It is also possible some of your ambivalent family members might be living with a Beast of their own. The world is full of all kinds of people, and so is your family.

 **Who are your family members who are ambivalent or non-supportive about your challenge?**

 **How do you feel about the fact that certain family members are ambivalent or non-supportive?**

**What can you do to move to a place of acceptance?**

*Momentary Connections*

Have you ever met someone and had an instant connection with them? Have you had a stranger say something that, to this day, you have never forgotten? Have you ever had an interaction with someone you have never seen again, yet every time you think about them, you feel happy or energized?

Momentary connections can help in unexpected ways. Kindness from strangers reminds us of our humanity. One brief comment can stay with us for the rest of our lives. In turn, an opportunity to extend a hand, or give a word of encouragement to someone we don't know, allows us to rise above our circumstances.

So, impactful are some of these brief encounters that I was tempted to include them in the Ring of Courage. Since they are chance encounters, they have been included in the Ring of Influence, but don't discount the importance of these moments. The next time you go shopping, out to dinner, or meet a stranger while on a walk, smile and say hello. Ask how the other person is doing. You never know when these momentary connection opportunities will present themselves.

**Have you ever met someone and had an instant connection with them?**

**Have you had a stranger say something that, to this day, you have never forgotten? What was it that they said and why was it impactful?**

**Are you staying open to these momentary connections, or do you go about your business without interacting with the people that you come into contact with?**

## Ring of Fire

*I fell into a burning ring of fire,*
*I went down, down, down, and the flames went higher*
*And it burns, burns, burns, the ring of fire.*
*— "Ring of Fire" by Johnny Cash*

The Ring of Fire in Your Circle of Strength is full of the people who are challenging to be in a relationship with. They might be a family member, an acquaintance, or a coworker. Typically, the people in your Ring of Fire are those people you can't easily avoid. If there are people in this group you can avoid, and are choosing not to, you may want to ask yourself why!

### Fair-Weather "Friends"

A fair-weather friend is one who is supportive only when it is convenient and easy, or when it benefits them. If a person is your friend when everything is going well but is conveniently absent when you're going through a rough patch, an argument could be made that they are not really a friend. Thus, a fair-weather friend could more appropriately be named, a fair-weather acquaintance.

These fair-weather people may be difficult for you to remove from your life. It might be your friend from childhood that you still feel bonded with due to your long history. Maybe she is your sister-in-law. Or it's the charismatic friend, that when you are with him, makes you forget he is selfish, until the next time he lets you down.

Fair-weather people may be hard to remove from your life, or you may not choose to do so. If a fair-weather friend is in your life by choice, then don't continue to be surprised by the inevitable disappointments you will experience. Be careful not to allow these relationships to influence your self-esteem or your sense of value as a friend. Take them for what they are worth.

 **The odds are that you have at least one fair-weathered friend. Who is it?**

 **Are you okay with the "fair-weathered" relationship you have with this person, or do you allow them to disappoint you time and time again?**

If you are not negatively impacted by this relationship, then you don't need to do anything about it. However, if you are overly disappointed by this person or have allowed the relationship to impact your self-worth, you should either work to change your attitude about the relationship or move away from the relationship. Only you can decide what is best for you.

 **Deep down, you know what is best for you. What are you going to do (if you need to do something) about this relationship, and when are you going to do it?**

*Negative Family*

Newsflash - not all family members will support you. It has been said, "familiarity breeds contempt." The more acquainted one becomes with another person, the more that person's shortcomings are known, resulting in a sense of disrespect. Who knows us better than our family? Our families should love us in spite of our shortcomings, but that is not always going to be the case.

Don't put too much pressure on your family. As with all of your relationships, you have a natural chemistry and bonding with people at different levels. It is the same way with your family. We choose our friends, but, for the most part, we don't choose our family.

There will invariably be people in your family that, given the choice, you would never have chosen. Typically, these people are negative, cynical and offensive about most things. Worse yet, they may be looking for company.

Negative people are hard to deal with in general and can be more of a challenge when they are family. You might choose to love these family members, but for your sake, limit the amount of time you spend with them. Unfortunately, negativity can be more contagious than positivity.

 **Who are your negative family members?**

You may need to stop and give this next question some serious thought. It is not easy to walk away from family members, even when they are negatively affecting your battle, recovery or attitude.

**What is your strategy for not allowing negative family members to impact you?**

Once you have begun to implement your strategy, there will no doubt be times when these family members will aggravate you. We all fall back into old patterns, so when this happens, come back to this page and reference your strategy. Get back on track with it, or modify the strategy.

### Unavoidable People

There are certain people, other than family members who are unavoidable. Often a co-worker can be as challenging, or more so than a negative family member. Many people spend more time with co-workers than nearly anyone else. Unless you're the boss, you don't get to choose your co-workers. If you have a co-worker who rubs you the wrong way, or worse yet, is incredibly negative, you will need to dig down deep in order to not be impacted by them.

Unavoidable people may be a spouse or family member of a friend, a customer, or a member of a club where you belong. If there is nothing you can do to avoid the person, you're going to have to put up an invisible shield. Don't let their negativity stick to you; try to let it slide right off of you.

For your sake, I hope you're not dealing with too many negative people. Do whatever you can to take these people in small doses.

 **Who are your unavoidable people, and how do you try not to let them affect you.**

### *The Ring of Fire Can Actually Help You*

After all of the warnings and cautions about the Ring of Fire, there is a silver lining. For much of the time, it may feel like more of a rust lining. There are some good things that can come out of the relationships with people you're "stuck with" in the Ring of Fire if you're willing to consider them.

First, negative or cynical people are a mirror. If you don't like what you see when you look into the Ring of Fire, be careful, you don't see yourself in its reflection.

Another benefit of the Ring of Fire is that it allows (or forces) you to develop patience, empathy, and tolerance.

If you can't avoid the Ring of Fire, why not take the opportunity to learn and grow from the people in that ring. When you look back, you might attribute some of your most important growth to the Ring of Fire.

 **What is the worst part of the Ring of Fire?**

 **What lessons have you already learned from the Ring of Fire?**

 **What are the ways in which the Ring of Fire has forced you to change or grow?**

Although we would all like to avoid the people in the Ring of Fire, we know that it's not possible. Therefore, take the opportunity to get the most you can out of the relationships and experiences in the Ring of Fire.

 **Can you see ways in which the Ring of Fire is beneficial?**

 **What are the ways in which you could change your outlook on some of the people in your Ring of Fire in order to take advantage of the opportunity for the people who rub you the wrong way, to smooth out your own rough edges?**

## Broken Heart Glue

If you're alive, you will undoubtedly suffer heartbreak. The very heart scars you think will take you down are those that will make you stronger. When muscles are overworked, the fibers are torn down. Through this process, the muscle fibers become scarred, leaving them stronger. In the same way, a broken heart will be left scarred, but once healed it will be stronger than ever.

Unhealed heartbreaks can keep us from ever deeply loving or trusting again. They can cause you to become bitter, cynical, and to lose hope.

Although there is no plastic surgeon for the heart, there is something better. It is called Broken Heart Glue, which is love. The first person who can help you to mend your broken heart is you. Without self-love, it will be more difficult for you to accept love from others. Love yourself enough to let others love you.

If you have a broken heart due to a loved one's Beast, there are no doubt, so many cracks in your heart that it's hard to tell where one starts, and another ends. If you have lost someone close to you, then you have a gaping wound. In any case, it will require many applications of Broken Heart Glue. Thankfully, there is a never-ending supply. Turn to your Circle of Strength; they are holding your tubes of Broken Heart Glue.

 **Who is holding your Broken Heart Glue? They will likely be people in your Inner Circle and Your Ring of Courage.**

 **Have you been reluctant to allow them to apply heart glue?**

 **If so, why?**

Often, we are afraid that our problem is too big, and that other people will not want to deal with it; we don't want to burden the people that we love. Consider, however, how you would feel if someone you loved needed you to help mend their broken heart, but they never asked. Wouldn't you want to give them your heart glue? Don't deny another person the joy and satisfaction of sharing their glue with you.

 **Who can you allow to offer their heart glue to you today?**

## Fitting the Pieces Together

Don't step onto the battlefield alone; **Build Your Circle of Strength**. Ultimately, you need to **Decide to Stand Up and Fight**, for yourself, but it might be your Circle of Strength that inspires, nudges or pushes you to make the decision. Your Circle of Strength will remind you when you need to **Change Your Attitude** or to **Adjust Your Focus**. Your Circle will believe in you when you find it hard to believe in yourself and stand with you as you **Stand <u>On</u> Your Story**. They will cheer you on as you **Make Meaning From the Madness**. Some of the people in your Circle of Strength will help you to **Put On Your Oxygen Mask** and to **Get On Your Spiritual Armor**. Others will simply raise their hand, reminding you they are there for you and you can let go and **Stop Being a Control Freak.**

## Your Declaration

Fill in the blanks of the Build Your Circle of Strength declaration as a reminder of the value and importance of your Circle of Strength.

---

### Build Your Circle of Strength Declaration

I, _____ am in a battle with a Beast. My Beast is: _____

_____

Today, _____, 20_____ I value the relationships in my Circle of Strength. I declare that I will work to strengthen my empowering relationships, and will stay away from negative and cynical people as much as possible. I declare that I will learn from each person in the Circle of Strength, even those in the Ring of Fire.

_____
Signed

---

## Faith in the Battle

*"If one person falls, the other can reach out and help. But someone who falls alone is in real trouble.* **Ecclesiastes 4:10 NLT**

When I found out my son was an addict, my Beast, like that of my son's, did everything in its power to isolate me. I did not want to be questioned or judged. It was all consuming, stealing from me my hope, energy, family, and friends. Perhaps you have the same Beast as I do, but no matter what Beast you struggle with, it will isolate you from the support system if you let it. People by nature are communal beings. God in his wisdom after creating Adam looked at him and said, "It is not good for the man to be alone. I will make a helper suitable for him." (Genesis 2:18.) Likewise, Jesus chose his disciples to be with him as he began his public ministry. Cunningly, the first thing our Beasts do is seek to pull us away from our support systems. As a mom whose son struggles with substance abuse disorder, I pulled away from others to focus solely on my son's Beast as I attempted to rescue him from its' clutches. I believed it was my job to fix him and so I immersed myself in that mission.

I was unavailable emotionally as a wife, and I lacked the time and energy to cultivate the friendships in my life. I didn't want to admit to anyone that our family had been ripped apart by my son's addiction, so I struggled alone. As I began to finally open up to those around me, it was like I was an objective reporter stating, "just the facts," void of any emotions for fear that in my vulnerability I would break down or be asked too many questions, most of which I would be unable to answer. How could I confess to those closest to me, my family, close friends, even my church friends that my biggest fear is that he might die and take some innocent bystander with him? How could I confess that I felt forgotten by God and that my heart stung like an old wound that refused to heal? There is a struggle within some churches to understand how addiction can step into a Christian family's life without the parents bearing some responsibility for its presence. Trying to avoid feeling any more shame than I already did, I decided to keep my family's struggles mainly to myself.

Shame is one of the primary weapons our Beasts use to keep us isolated and silent. Our Beast convinces us that no one will understand or that they will judge us or blame us. It convinces us that we should just be able to get over it and get on with our lives. Shame keeps us silent and isolated, and that is just the way the Beast wants us to stay. I love Valerie's diagram of the Circle of Strength. It helps me realize which ring I should place people in. The ones who tried to expose me and make me feel guilt and shame were moved into the Ring of Fire, making room for some very special people to fit into my Inner Circle, Ring of Courage, and Ring of Influence.

**Look up the following scriptures:**

**Mark 12:30-31**

**John 15:12-13**

**What do these verses teach you about the love of God?**

**What do they tell you about loving your neighbor?**

Agape is the Greek word for the selfless, unconditional, divine love of God. As you read the following verses from the "Love Chapter," ask the Lord to help you build your Circle of Strength with trusted friends and advisors who meet the qualifications and will stand with you in this battle.

**Look up 1 Corinthians 13:4-8a and fill in the blanks describing God's love.**

*"Love is _____, love is _____. It does not _____, it does not _____, it is not _____. It does not _____ others, it is not _____, it is not _____ _____, it keeps no _____ of _____. Love does not delight in _____, but rejoices with the _____. It always _____, always _____, always_____, always _____. Love never _____.*

**Now that you have a deeper understanding of God's love, look up and write out the following scriptures to gain a better understanding of your friends and family and note how they fit into your Circle of Strength.**

**Proverbs 17:17**

**Ephesians 4:2**

**1 John 3:18**

One thing I have learned through this experience is that people surprise me. The other is that I surprise myself. The ones I expected to be supportive may pretend to be but cannot wait to change the subject usually because the topic is difficult and they feel awkward discussing it. On the other hand, I have been floored by the kindness of some people and how supportive they have been. My father and step-mother, for instance, did not find out about my son's addiction until years into it. The truth is that I waited to tell them until a few months before she died from terminal cancer. When I finally broke down and told them, I expected harsh words and judgment; instead, I was greeted with love, tears, and a desire to help their grandson. I thought about how I had misjudged them for so long and allowed my pride to keep me from opening up to an awesome support system. Because of the pain of my childhood, I foolishly built walls, not boundaries, and shut out the very people who would have loved and supported us through this. Isn't that just like the heart of God to wrap his love up in unexpected packages?

 **Look back at your Circle of strength and examine your friendships and relationships with family members, friends, and acquaintances. Based on your understanding of God's love and how he wants us to treat each other, are there**

**any changes you need to make in where and how your relationships fit into your Circle of Strength?**

**If so, why?**

 **Are there any areas that you personally need to address so that you can be part of someone's Circle of Strength, having a positive impact when they are hurting?**

*"Now about your love for one another we do not need to write to you, for you yourselves have been taught by God to love each other."* **1 Thessalonians 4:9**

Finally, let's take a look at relationships that perhaps should be part of our Ring of Fire. These include the fair-weather friends, negative family, and unavoidable people who say what they think, often without thinking. We all have those people in our lives that know right where to hit us when we are down. Recognizing them is fairly easy, but being able to place them into our Ring of Fire actually empowers us to take away some of their power to hurt us. As we consider the source, we can learn to limit our exposure to them and how much their opinion negatively impacts us.

 **Look up these verses and note the characteristics of someone who may belong in your Ring of Fire:**

**Proverbs 16:28**

**Ephesians 4:31-32**

**Proverbs 27:6**

**After reflecting on these scriptures, are there people you may need to move into your Ring of Fire?**

**How will you limit your exposure to them and their ability to have a negative impact on you?**

**As you place them into your Ring of Fire, are you able to forgive them and let go of any unrealistic expectations you may have of them?**

**If this is an area you are struggling in, take it and this person to the Lord now and choose to move forward in forgiveness.**

*"Forgive us our sins, for we also forgive everyone who sins against us."* **Luke 11:4**

Friendship has a way of finding you in the most interesting of places. I met Valerie after purchasing a copy of her book. Unfortunately, (but fortunately for me), my copy did not download, so I contacted her via email to ask her to re-send it. Somehow, we started communicating, and it was the beginning of a dear friendship. There are many things that bond Valerie and me together, our sense of humor, our boldness, our faith in God. Oh, and we both have addicted children. There was no way to know that I would be writing this chapter of Faith in the Battle when Valerie would learn of the tragic death of her daughter, Jamie (whom she called "Jordan" in her books). How could I expect to be anywhere in her Circle of Strength, much less part of her Inner Circle? It was impossible for me to understand the loss, the pain, and the grief she was experiencing. From the beginning of our relationship, we both knew that God had brought us together for a reason. I fought to believe that somehow with his help I could be there to love her in her pain and remind her of the tremendous love and faithfulness of God that endures through the darkest paths life would take her on. I also knew I had so much more I could learn by observing rather than speaking. I learned to watch closely at the tenderness of God as he held her and loved her in ways that were beyond my understanding. She has quickly become one of my rare Foxhole Friends. She loved and cared about me and others when she hurt the most. She prayed for my son as well as many other addicts and their moms when she still had yet to bury her own. She reached out to others who needed to fight their Beasts when she was still grieving her own loss. What kind of love is this? It is the love of God, and when we receive that love into our lives, we are able to share his Broken Heart Glue with others who are hurting, and that is exactly what she did and is still doing.

No matter where you end up being in another's Circle of Strength, it's okay. We can't be all things to all people nor can they be all things to us. Just try not to end up in anyone's Ring of Fire. Whether you are a Foxhole Friend or in their Ring of Influence, you have the ability to breathe hope into their circumstances. Pray about how much or how little involvement you should have in this person's life. There are seasons where the Lord may have you take a step back and quietly support them from a distance. There are also times when he will call you to press in and stand with them in the tough stuff. You were put in that person's circle for a reason, even if it is just for a momentary connection. Who knows though? It could just be that you will soon be lifetime friends!

*"Therefore, encourage one another and build each other up, just as, in fact, you are doing."*
**1Thessalonians 5:11**

*"Be courteous to all, but intimate with few, and let those few be well tried before you give them your confidence."*
**George Washington**

## *Action #5: Change Your Attitude*

TM

*"No matter what your attitude is, it will influence others. Do you want to influence others with negativity, self-pity, and cynicism? Or would you rather promote happiness and hope? You have the power to choose."*

— **Valerie Silveira**

## Attitude Introduction

There is nothing you can do to change what has happened in the past. There will be things that happen in the future, for which you have no control. There may be but one thing in life you can truly control - your attitude. We get to choose every single day, in every situation, in each moment, what our attitude will be. There have been plenty of times I didn't have the right attitude. Countless words have flown out of my mouth that I wished I could take back. A bad attitude will always lead to negative words spoken and negative actions taken.

The right attitude will result in words of encouragement, hope, and inspiration. A positive attitude will lead you to take positive actions. Have you ever had a great attitude and regretted it afterward?

Whether negative or positive, your attitude has an influence on those around you. Do you want to influence others with negativity, self-pity, and cynicism? Or would you rather promote happiness and hope? You have the power to choose. Attitude is a battle changer.

 **Do you have a desire to take control of your attitude and believe you have the power to do so?**

## Logic of a Negative Thinker

My childhood was challenging. Gone was a very young mother's college dream, along with, for the most part, the father of her three children. It was during those early years, sitting by the window waiting for my dad that I gave myself the first of many lessons on negativity.

In those days, we only had play clothes and school clothes. When we were to go with our dad, we got into our school clothes and waited for him to arrive. I sat with my two brothers on the sofa, looking out the window. Many times, he didn't show up. On those occasions, we would get off the couch and into our pajamas. As a disappointed little girl, I plodded off to my room with the dwindling hope that next time would be different.

I was tired of being disappointed by my dad; by many things in my young life. I developed a mentality that helped me to avoid disappointment. My philosophy was that if I thought the worst, I would never be disappointed. If something good happened, I would consider it a bonus.

Not only did I begin to live by that negative thinking, but I shared it with anyone who would listen! It horrifies me now to considering the negativity I perpetuated with my negative thinking logic.

Negative thinking may help to avoid disappointment, but it sure is a waste of a lot of time in between. Consider the number of hours, days, weeks, months, or even years in between disappointments that you live in darkness, without hope. It's not worth it.

If you are in a negative mode, it should come as no surprise when one thing after the next seems to go south in your life, or that you begin to attract negative people like flies at a picnic. On the contrary, when you *expect* the best, you may be surprised when *coincidentally* more positive people and situations come your way.

 **Do you want to influence others with negativity, self-pity, and cynicism?**

 **Or would you rather promote happiness and hope?**

## Pity Party

It is easy to end up at a Pity Party. They have nonstop advertising, aggressive marketing, and huge welcoming committees. If there were actual buildings, they would have easy to find, well-lit entrances, and greeters at the doors. The minute you arrive at a

Pity Party, you will feel welcome. Strangers only moments before will become long lost friends.

Pity Party goers are not solution finders; they are waiting for someone else to swoop in and fix their problems. Regular attendees at Pity Parties seem to be happy only when they are unhappy.

If you find yourself at a Pity Party, it's advisable to head for the nearest exit. Unfortunately, finding an exit from a Pity Party will prove challenging. In contrast to the warm welcome, few people will help you locate the exit door. The closer you get the more resistance you will have from the other attendees. If you do find one, it will be a small, unmarked door at the end of a maze. Once you locate the exit, run for the door and don't look back. Better yet, decline the invitation.

As tough as it is to extricate yourself from a Pity Party, it will prove even more so to leave a party that you have hosted. Throwing your guests out once you have invited them is much more problematic than excusing yourself from another person's Pity Party. It is best to stay as far away from Pity Parties as you can.

 **Are you currently in attendance at a Pity Party?**

 **Who are the other people in your life that attend the party with you?**

 **Do you want to get out of the Pity Party?**

It is a challenge to leave a Pity Party. It is going to take some courage and determination to leave and to stay away. Especially if there are others close to you, who attend the same party. If you stop feeling overly sorry for yourself, begin to take positive action and speak victory over your problem, you may not have to leave - the others may throw you out!

**What can you start doing today that will move you closer to the exit door of the Pity Party, or better yet, be asked to leave?**

## Two Types of Victims

If you are a victim due to the actions of another person, or a situation you were not in control of, then you truly are a victim. There is nothing wrong with acknowledging you have been victimized and giving yourself permission to process the emotions that come along with being a victim. There may be medical, psychological, financial, and legal issues to wade through. Certainly, those things need to be handled.

Becoming a victim may not have been your fault, but continuing to live as one is your choice. No matter which of life's two-by-fours smacked you over the head, you can decide whether or not you will remain living as a victim.

There are two types of victims, the Poor Me Victim and the Victim in Disguise.

### Poor Me Victim

Poor Me Victims constantly solicit sympathy either directly or indirectly. Some Poor Me Victims will make it clear they want and expect your pity. Others take a more passive-aggressive approach when it comes to eliciting sympathy. These people will act as if they don't want your sympathy, but drop continuous hints or make off-handed comments, in hopes, you will pity them or come to their rescue.

Neither tactic works well in the long run for the Poor Me Victim. Initially, people will respond with sympathy, but eventually, they will grow weary, especially if the Poor Me Victim is not trying to change their circumstances or their attitude. Over time, a Poor Me Victim will be left with only other Poor Me Victims, or with people who feel obligated to be in a relationship with them.

*Victim in Disguise*

The second type of victim is the Victim in Disguise. These victims are strong; the people others rely on for strength and support. Not used to being needy, the Victim in Disguise is skilled at masking their pain.

Victims in Disguise are terrified of being considered victims, so they wear a mask to hide the pain, and then go home and cry themselves to sleep. Unlike the Poor Me Victim, Victims in Disguise may believe they need little to no support, and then find it hurtful when nobody offers.

Victims in Disguise may even try to convince themselves they are not in a battle or have won it when the truth is they have simply learned to exist with their Beast. I was a Victim in Disguise.

Neither victim is a healthy way to live. Whether a Poor Me Victim or a Victim in Disguise, it is time to conquer the Beast and step out of victimhood.

 **Did you identify yourself as being either a Poor Me Victim or a Victim in Disguise?**

 **Are you ready to move away from being a victim?**

 **What are the top three reasons that you want to stop being a Poor Me Victim or a Victim in Disguise?**

1.

2.

3.

 **Identify three things that you can begin to do that will move you away from being a victim.**

1.

2.

3.

## Coulda, Shoulda, Woulda

When Jordan and Sean were young, I would tell them there are three people you really need to avoid: Coulda, Shoulda, and Woulda. It would have served me well to listen to my own advice. Living with my Beast for nearly 13 years, I developed a very close relationship with Coulda, Shoulda, and Woulda. So familiar were they to me that I named them.

### *Mea Coulda*

Mea Coulda tells you what you could have done differently. She is the image you have conjured up in your mind of the stress-free life you could only dream of living. Mea Coulda has escaped pain and heartbreak, floating through life without a care in the world. Mea has the life you *could* have had; if only you had been luckier.

### *Shirley Shoulda*

Shirley Shoulda preys on shame and guilt. Unlike *your* hindsight, Shirley Shoulda's foresight is 20/20. Shirley Shoulda is a know it all, and never misses an opportunity to get what she wants. Shirley Shoulda makes you doubt and regret every decision you have made and every action you have taken, or not taken. Shirley Shoulda never lets you forget what you *should* have done differently.

### *I. Woulda*

Everything I. Woulda touches turns to gold. I. Woulda represents every person you have ever stood in awe of, wondering what it takes to live without ever making a mistake.

I. Woulda would never make a bad financial decision. He would never be in an unhealthy relationship, depressed, betrayed, abandoned or unloved. Certainly, he would never have a child who is an addict.

I. Woulda is a constant reminder that other people are living worry-free, successful, productive lives. You could have too, if only you *would* have made different decisions.

### *Quit Hanging Out With Them*

Mea Coulda, Shirley Shoulda, and I. Woulda are obviously not real people. They are life-like examples of our self-talk. When life goes sideways, we spend a great deal of time considering what we could have, should have, or would have done differently. Mea Coulda, Shirley Shoulda, and I. Woulda will keep you trapped in the past, beating yourself up over every move you have made, or not made.

Visiting the past can be helpful in understanding how or why certain things have transpired, or why you have developed certain characteristics. It can help you to avoid making the same mistakes.

Continuous trips into the past, especially with Coulda, Shoulda, and Woulda will keep you stuck where you are.

You know you need to throw them out of your life, but you keep inviting them back. Each time Mea Coulda, Shirley Shoulda, or I. Woulda show up, show them the door. This line of thinking is self-destructive and is sure to gain you express entrance to a Pity Party.

 **What do you see as the biggest problem with spending too much time with Mea Coulda, Shirley Shoulda, and I. Woulda?**

**Keep track for one week (or even one day) of how many times you say: could've, should've or would've. # Days _____ # Times _____**

## If You Spoke to Others the Way You Speak to Yourself

I attended a three-day women's golf camp at our club a few years back. One afternoon, a sports psychologist gave a talk to the group.

She said, "If you spoke to others the way you speak to yourself on the golf course, nobody would ever play golf with you."

The room fell silent, other than the sounds of women shifting in their seats. My guess is the guilty look on the faces of the other women mirrored my own expression.

Women golfers tend to be very complimentary and encouraging of one another, but not so with themselves. I have watched women beat themselves up like Dobby the House Elf in the Harry Potter stories. I was Dobby, flogging myself for years on the golf course, and in many other situations.

You should avoid negative people. However, it is a little more challenging to avoid a negative person when that person is you.

We could apply the same psychology we learned at golf camp to other areas of our lives. If you spoke to others the way you too often speak to yourself, you wouldn't have many friends.

 **Are you speaking to yourself the way you want others to speak to you?**

**Try to go an entire day without saying anything negative about yourself; it may be harder than you think. Did you make it all day? If not, how long was it before you said something negative about yourself?**

## Ten Percent of My Life

A couple of years ago, I reconnected with some of my high school friends. We were having dinner, and I looked across the table at Christine when it occurred to me that I had never seen her with short hair. She always wore her thick, dark hair, long. I said across the table, "Christine, I've never seen you with short hair; you look great." The friend next to me elbowed me and whispered that Christine had battled cancer - twice. I turned red and apologized, telling Christine I wished I had known so I could have at least offered a word of encouragement.

Her reply is frozen in my mind.

"I purposely didn't tell a lot of people because I wanted this thing to take up about ten percent of my life."

She only wanted cancer to take up ten percent of her life! If you want to change your attitude, get around some people like Christine - the 10% of my life people. Better yet, work to be a 10% of my life person. You won't get there all at once, but it is a good goal to work toward.

 **List any "10% of my life" people you know.**

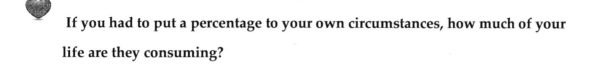 **If you had to put a percentage to your own circumstances, how much of your life are they consuming?**

**Is that percentage acceptable to you?**

# The Power of Attitude

## *Attitude, by Charles Swindoll*

*Attitude, by Charles Swindoll*

*The longer I live, the more I realize the impact of attitude on life.*

*It is more important than the facts.*

*It is more important than the past,*

*than education, than money,*

*than circumstances, than failures, than successes,*

*than what other people think or say or do.*

*It is more important than appearance, giftedness or skill.*

*The remarkable thing is we have a choice*

*every day of our lives regarding the attitude*

*we embrace for that day.*

*We can't change our past.*

*We can't change the fact that people*

*will act in a certain way.*

*We can't change the inevitable.*

*The only thing we can do is play on the one string we have,*

*and that is our attitude.*

*I am convinced that life is ten percent what happens to me*

*and ninety percent how I react to it.*

*And so, it is with you.*

*We are in charge of our attitudes.*

There is something in your control that acts as a weapon, with the potential to affect countless people. In the hands of the wrong person, this weapon is a toxic contagion, infecting everyone it comes into contact with. It cannot be contained or locked in a vault to avoid infection. The only way to stop this noxious contagion is to alter it. The weapon is a negative attitude, and the only way to stop it is to change it.

Negativity doesn't take a great deal of effort; most people tend to lean toward negativity. If you want to stay in the negative attitude zone, you will have plenty of help. You need only to watch the news, read the paper or talk with your neighbor. Truthfully, you don't have to turn on the television, pick up the paper or leave the house. It may be as easy as listening to your own thoughts.

Within you is a powerful force, that when unleashed, is just as contagious as the negative attitude toxin. It is your positive attitude.

Forty years later, someone will talk about the time you said something that helped to build the foundation for their positive attitude.

You may not have the power to change every situation, but in all situations, you do have the power to choose your attitude. In a battle with a Beast, a positive attitude is a battle changer.

 **Reflect on recent events and consider ways in which your attitude could have been more positive:**

 **Is it possible that a positive attitude might have altered the final outcome of a certain situation?**

## Fitting the Pieces Together

As you work to **Change Your Attitude**, other areas of your life will change too. The right attitude will prompt you to **Decide to Stand Up and Fight**. The ability to **Get On Your Spiritual Armor** and to **Put On Your Oxygen Mask** will be greatly influenced by your attitude. The right attitude will allow you to **Build Your Circle of Strength** faster and stronger. Without a positive attitude, it will be nearly impossible to **Adjust Your Focus** or to **Stop Being a Control Freak**. Your attitude will influence your decision to **Stand <u>On</u> Your Story** rather than in it and will push you to **Make Meaning From the Madness**

## Your Declaration

Complete the blanks of the Attitude Declaration. This is your chance to declare your change of attitude. It will remind you that your attitude is a battle changer.

---

### Change Your Attitude Declaration

I, _____ am in a battle with a Beast. My Beast is: _____

_____

Today, _____, 20_____ I know that Attitude is my battle changer. I declare that I will be more aware of my attitude & work to change it. I will become a woman or man who impacts the world with my new attitude.

_____
Signed

---

## Faith in the Battle

**Attitude**, noun-a **settled** way of thinking or feeling about someone or something, typically one that is reflected in a person's **behavior**.

Changing our attitudes is hard work, but it is necessary if we ever hope to change our behavior. It requires concentrated effort and practice to achieve our goals, even if it is "just" an attitude adjustment. Like training for a marathon or learning to play the piano, changing our behavior requires first developing discipline in our attitudes, in what we think, and how we speak. It is much easier to listen to and act on negative thinking than to make the decision to change our attitudes for the better. Have you ever noticed when one person in a group starts to complain, the whole group will start to chime in? Just like water follows down the path of least resistance, so do our attitudes.

It is habit-forming to think negatively because it comes so naturally to us. Why? Because life is hard, that's why! I would have loved to learn the Lord's life lessons for me another way and by taking an easier route but that wasn't the case. Truthfully, I was becoming resentful, and although I did not realize it at first, I had taken on a victim mentality. I, like Valerie, was more of a Victim in Disguise, at least for the most part. Get me alone with my husband, though, and the Poor-Me victim would rear its ugly head. Likewise, everyone can risk becoming victims of their circumstances as well, if they do not carefully watch their attitudes. How can we change our attitudes if we are living in the past or afraid of the future? Mea Coulda, Shirley Shoulda, and I. Woulda would love to hold our attitudes hostage to negative thinking. Like Valerie reminded us earlier, we need to quit hanging out with them.

*"You were taught, with regard to your former way of life, to put off your old self, which is being corrupted by its deceitful desires; to be made new in the attitude of your minds; and to put on the new self, created to be like God in true righteousness and holiness."* **Ephesians 4:22-24**

No matter what Beasts have controlled our lives up until this point, it is our attitude that will determine if we will ever be free from the hold they have on us. The first step is always the hardest because it means letting go, and if we are really going to let go, we need to "give up." You've heard the old saying, "let go and let God." I say, "give up and give it to God." The Christian life is about giving up our will and surrendering to God and His plan and purpose. For some of us, it means surrendering our children to him and trusting that he will accomplish his purpose in their lives. For others, it means no longer trying to control everything and everyone, but letting go and trusting him with the results. And for others, it may mean moving past the hold that depression or a bad marriage or even health issues have on them. Easier said than done, I know, but as we release our negative thinking and make a choice to not attend our own pity party as the guest of honor, we will begin to see these trials as opportunities to become better and stronger.

**Look up the following scriptures. Write them out:**

**Philippians 2:5**

**Romans 12:2**

**Colossians 3:1-2**

**According to these verses, what are we told to do regarding our thinking and attitudes?**

**What areas do you struggle with?**

When I decided enough was enough, and I wanted off the Roller Coaster from Hell, I was in need of a big attitude change. That would be easier said than done, but the Lord always gives us what we need to obey His will, so let's delve into this a little deeper.

**Look at Philippians 4.**

*4:4 - Rejoice in the Lord always. I will say it again: Rejoice!*

*4:5 - Let your gentleness be evident to all. The Lord is near.*

*4:6– Do not be anxious about anything, but in every situation, by prayers and petition, with thanksgiving, present your requests to God.*

*4:7- And the peace of God, which transcends all understanding, will guard your hearts and your minds in Christ Jesus.*

**4:8-** *Finally, brothers and sisters, whatever is true, whatever is noble, whatever is right, whatever is pure, whatever is lovely, whatever is admirable- if anything is excellent or praiseworthy- think about such things.*

**Go back to each verse and draw a CIRCLE around or Highlight what you are told TO DO. Next, draw a RECTANGLE around or Highlight using a different color what you are told NOT TO DO. Finally, underline the promises of God for you in these verses.**

Here we learn to change our attitudes by reflecting on the positive. One of the first and best ways to change our attitudes is to realize that God is helping us to do just that. He gave us a wealth of instructions in verse 8 on what we should do if we want our lives to be full of peace and not overwhelmed with anxiety and fear.

 **Look now at verses 4:11-12 and write it out.**

Paul talks about how he **learned** to be **content** in all circumstances and in every situation. Content here means "satisfied with what one is or has; not wanting more or anything else." Paul stated that he "had learned" how to be content, which is a good indicator that at one time he was probably the opposite of content, miserable. How is it that Paul, being held up in a prison cell, could say that he had learned to be content in all circumstances? After all, he had every excuse to be miserable, didn't he? But Paul

161

realized that life had handed him many opportunities to learn how to be content, so he chose to submit to God's plan even if it meant going through some really hard stuff.

I believe this "secret" to being content that Paul talked about is submission to accepting the things we cannot change and trusting in God's will for our lives as well as our loved one's lives. Instead, we want to control or fix the things and people that make us uncomfortable or cause us fear or pain. We want a crystal ball to see into the future and prevent that pain altogether or at least control the collateral damage it causes. It all comes back to wanting to be in control of our own lives and destinies, but it doesn't work that way. We live in a broken, fallen world that has more pain and suffering than we can ever imagine. Yet, the Lord has promised peace and contentment as we surrender to him. Paul had the right attitude in his suffering; he made the choice to be content. Verse 13 tells us how: "I can do all this through him who gives me strength."

Finally, a change in our attitude is possible when we begin to see our situation as God sees it. **Romans 12:9** says, "Love must be sincere. Hate what is evil; cling to what is good." The literal translation for sincere love is "love without hypocrisy." The New Living Translation says, "Don't just pretend to love others. Really love them. Hate what is wrong. Hold tightly to what is good." So, this is where the rubber meets the road. When we begin to see our situation as God sees it, we will no longer allow another's poor choices and irresponsible actions to draw us away from our one true Source of love, peace, and contentment. Sincere love clings to God. It stops living in negativity. It's no longer controlled by regret. It loves each other with the same love that Christ loves us. In doing so, our attitude change comes from a deeper heart change.

 **Look up and write out the following scriptures.**

**Romans 15:5**

**Ephesians 4:22-24**

**Do you have a desire to take control of your attitude and believe you have the power to do so?**

**In closing, go back and reconsider this question that Valerie asked earlier and ask yourself if you are truly ready, willing, and able to move forward with changing your attitude.**

*"...Forgetting what is behind and straining toward what is ahead, I press on toward the goal to win the prize for which God has called me heavenward in Christ Jesus."*

**Philippians 3:13b-14**

*"I don't think of all the misery, but of the beauty that still remains."*

**Anne Frank**

*"Don't compare your Beast to someone else's. Don't worry if yours is bigger, smaller, easier, or harder. Stay focused on your own journey; on battling your own Beast."*

— **Valerie Silveira**

## Action Introduction

When all hell breaks loose, it's natural for your perspective to get out of focus. During your darkest days, it will appear everyone but you has what you don't have.

The more time you spend focused on another person, longing for their life, the more convinced you will become, that your life is never going to change. The gap between the imaginary perfect life others are enjoying, and yours will continuously widen.

Before long, it will feel as if you are standing at the Grand Canyon. On one side, you stand with your troubles, with your Beast. Eighteen miles across, standing on the other side, are all of the other people who have somehow escaped life's misfortune. As you look longingly across the great expanse, straining to see the faces of those more fortunate, you will miss one simple fact - everybody has a story.

Standing there feeling alone, turn around and take a look beside you and behind you. As far as your eye can see, and beyond, will be those who have been where you are, or worse. Everybody has a story.

## Keep Your Social Media Microscope in Focus

Social media has allowed us to connect with people we have lost contact with, and to stay in touch with friends and family. Thankfully, most people have chosen to post the happiest and most positive aspects of their lives on social media platforms, which have become *go-to* places for inspiration and motivation. However, let me issue you a warning:

*"Lives Lived Out on Social Media*

*May Appear Better Than They Really Are"*

*— Valerie Silveira*

Although positive news is much better than the alternative, social media can leave us with a false sense of others' lives in comparison to ours.

What you focus on becomes magnified. When you experience loss, it's natural to become more aware of what others have. The more loss I felt as Jordan moved deeper into her addiction, the more it appeared every other mother had a perfect daughter.

To my aching heart, Facebook posts seemed to appear daily stating people had the "best daughter in the world." They went on to suggest I share the post if I too, had a daughter I was proud of, who meant the world to me, and so on. There were times when I didn't even know where my daughter was, or even if she were alive.

It wasn't just the "world's best daughter" posts; it was everything. Suddenly it appeared the entire world had the best husband, drank the best wine, went on weekly dream vacations, swam with the dolphins, drove the coolest cars, had the best friends in the world and bulging bank accounts - perfect lives. The postings were not the problem. Clearly, I was out of focus.

Be careful not to spend too much time focused on momentary messages. Nobody has a perfect "anything." During a battle with a Beast, you will need to re-focus constantly in order to maintain perspective. Some people have what you don't, but it's counter-productive to focus on another person's journey. Most of them are not what they appear to be anyway.

**Have you found yourself feeling envious or jealous of your perception of others' lives?**

## Everybody Has a Story

If you are peering through the window of somebody else's life and it looks perfect, chances are they haven't cleaned their windows in a while. Other people's lives are not perfect in spite of how they may appear to you. The same darkness comes upon everybody at night. The same sun rises in the morning.

Everybody has challenges and struggles. We all know people whose lives are easier than ours, and I have no explanation for that, but it's useless to spend valuable time attempting to figure it out, and it doesn't matter anyway.

When it appears what you're going through is far more challenging than others around you, it could be a timing issue. While you're feeling your way around in the dark, or battling a Beast, you're sure everyone else is on a beach sipping drinks with umbrellas in them. Life happens in cycles, and there will come a time when each person will have some type of challenge.

 **Have you made an assumption that a certain person had no hardship or pain in their life only to discover something about them that you didn't know?**

 **Who was it and what was the situation?**

## It's Time to Start a New Movie

Stephanie has a fear of abandonment from early childhood. Her father had all but abandoned her, leaving her mother to raise Stephanie and her brothers and sisters. She had a happy childhood, but Stephanie couldn't seem to get past her father's decision to leave, or the shame and anger she felt toward the addiction Beast he had yet to conquer.

Although not yet thirty, Stephanie longed to find a husband. She became hyper-focused on her married friends and became convinced she had a flaw or many flaws that kept her from meeting her future husband. By all accounts, Stephanie is a beautiful person, yet she has low self-esteem.

Stephanie met Adam and was sure she had finally met the one. He had all of the qualities Stephanie had been looking for; she was sure of it because she had a list, and one by one, she placed a check mark next to each quality Adam possessed. He already had a successful career; he was handsome, drove an expensive sports car, owned a condo overlooking the city and had tons of friends. Everyone loved Adam, including Stephanie.

Things were going well for a few months, but then Adam started to be a bit distant. He forgot to call her, broke dates claiming he had to work late at the office and was remiss in returning her calls. Stephanie feared that Adam was going to leave her so she did everything she could to be better.

Each time perfect Adam let her down, Stephanie tried harder to look better; to act better. The more distant he became, the more Stephanie tried to change, and the more she tried to hang on to Adam.

Eventually, Stephanie's worst fear was realized when Adam broke up with her. Stephanie was devastated. She went over every detail of her relationship with Adam and agonized over what she could have done differently. The all too familiar feelings of abandonment from her father surfaced, and she became depressed.

Stephanie was out of focus in a couple of different ways. First, Adam was not perfect, and, in fact, had demonstrated he was not who she thought he was. Instead of recognizing that, Stephanie chose to blame herself for the breakup.

Next, Stephanie was relating a broken relationship with a guy to her feelings of abandonment as a result of her father. She was having a hard time understanding that everyone goes through breakups, and most people have been through several failed love relationships over their lifetime.

If Stephanie can find a way to recall the true events of the relationship with Adam and to separate her feelings of abandonment with her father, from other relationships, she will begin to stare down her Beast.

Stephanie has a choice which movies she wants to run in her mind. She can continue to replay the breakup and abandonment movies, or she can choose to replay movies reminding her of all the people who have stood by her; far more than the one who abandoned her.

We have to be very careful we don't keep playing the same movie and expect a different ending. Sometimes it is time to pop in a new movie.

**Have you been running a movie (or movies) that you know you need to change?**

**What movies are you running through your mind over and over and hoping for a different outcome?**

## Cycle of Hope and Massive Disappointment

Disappointment is the result of unmet expectations. In healthy relationships, it's reasonable to have certain expectations. In a marriage, for example, we should expect our spouse to be faithful. Our children are expected to follow the rules at home and school. It isn't wrong to expect certain things from personal relationships.

Disappointment occurs when we place unrealistic expectations on others. It is reasonable to trust your child in your home. If that child is a drug addict who has stolen from you in the past, then it would be unrealistic for you to expect different behavior while they are using. In Stephanie's case, it would be unrealistic for her to expect her father to be there for her when he hasn't been since Stephanie was a young girl.

Each time you place unrealistic expectations on another person, it will invariably be followed by disappointment. We should continue to expect certain behaviors or levels of trust in our relationships, but we need to manage those expectations.

When someone shows you by their actions, who they are, believe them. People can and do change, but until they demonstrate otherwise, be careful placing expectations that you know in your heart will set you up for massive disappointment.

Managing disappointment and trying to live with hope can be a bit of a balancing act. Having a daughter for an addict keeps me constantly walking the tightrope, in an attempt to balance the two. For years, I lived in a constant cycle of hope and massive disappointment. I never want to lose hope that one day Jordan will finally tame her Beast, but if my hopes are too high, they will likely be followed by massive disappointment.

The statistics for an addict beating heroin are very low. Understanding the statistics, I still hope, pray and encourage Jordan to be one of the few that beat it. Still, I need to manage my hope and expectations with the reality of the situation.

You too need to manage expectations. You should strive to have a positive and hopeful attitude while avoiding the highs and devastating lows, particularly if your Beast is related to another person's Beast.

The hope and disappointment grid is an example of some of the highs and lows I have experienced and demonstrates movement toward more of a balance between hope and disappointment.

## CYCLE OF HOPE AND DISAPPOINTMENT

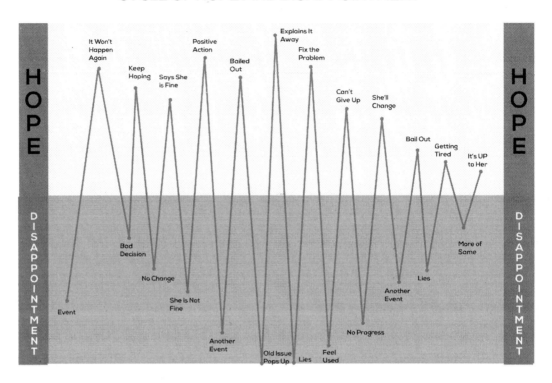

The idea is to avoid extreme highs followed by devastating lows. You will fall into the disappointment zone at times. The goal is to find your way back into the hope zone.

**Have you found yourself living in a cycle of hope and disappointment?**

**What have you done, or can you do to manage your expectations?**

**Can you identify spikes in hope, followed by massive disappointment in your life?**

**Use the following graph with my personal events removed to paint a picture of your own cycle of hope and disappointment. Fill in keywords to identify your highs and lows in a particular situation.**

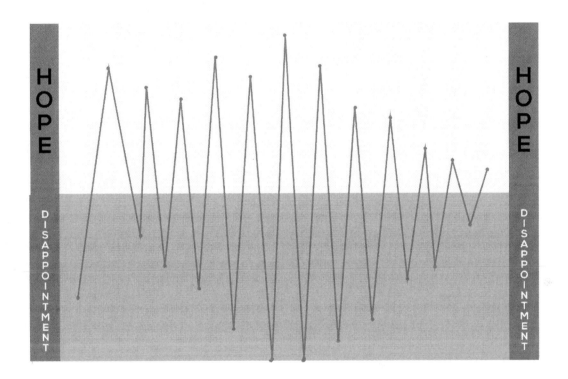

## Isolation

The longer Jordan was lost, the more I began to retreat. I wore out the movie of the life I *should have* had with my daughter, and each time I did, the more heartbroken I became. It was increasingly more difficult to hide my emotions; to pretend I was fine. It became easier to isolate myself.

When offered an invitation to meet new people or to socialize with friends, I did everything I could to decline. I had a list of excuses but didn't want to disappoint Rich, so I only used them when I was too exhausted to pretend. If not for my husband, I may have opted out of all social engagements.

In a situation of ongoing grief, you feel very alone, regardless of the number of loving people around you. I didn't know anyone with a child who is an addict, so I felt very isolated.

This story that illustrates what I was allowing to happen to me; possibly, what you are allowing to happen to you:

## The Old Woman in the Cave

Victoria was walking down the street one day when she stopped at a wide hole in the ground. Years before she had noticed a small crack in the same spot. Over time, the crack grew wider and deeper, but Victoria chose to ignore it. When she walked down that street, she crossed to the other side and looked the other way.

On this particular day, Victoria could no longer ignore the gaping hole. She stood at the edge and peered down into what was now a sinkhole, a good two feet below the surface. As she studied the hole, she lost her footing and toppled in, head first. She sat upright and struggled to make it to her knees, but she was starting to sink.

Victoria attempted to crawl to the edge, certain she could pull herself up, but with each movement, she sank deeper into the muck. She neared the edge when the soft earth gave way. Within seconds, she was up to her neck and gasping for breath.

She opened her mouth to scream for help, but it was too late; Victoria was pulled below the surface, and the earth closed in over her head. Deeper and deeper she sunk, and as quickly as it sucked her in, the earth spit her out. She landed on her backside in the dark.

Victoria stood up and put her hands out in front of her, moving forward until she met with a smooth rock wall. Feeling her way along the wall, she came to an adjacent wall and then another. She was at the end of a tunnel. Terrified, she turned around and stepped into the unknown.

Her eyes adjusted just enough to keep from running into the sides of the tunnel as it twisted and turned. Up ahead she saw light coming from a small opening in the tunnel wall.

Bending down, Victoria peeked into a spacious cave. At the far end of the lit, cave room sat an old woman at a rickety table, dabbing at her eyes with a worn handkerchief.

Victoria moved inside and stood up. The old woman didn't seem to notice her, so Victoria walked softly toward her and stood near the table. Eventually, the old woman glanced up at her with lifeless eyes.

She slowly stood and hobbled to a pot-bellied stove, and began to stir something that smelled dreadful. Victoria asked the old woman what she was doing in the cave, but she didn't respond.

The old woman set the spoon down and moved painfully to a single bed that sat opposite the room from the stove. She perched herself on the edge of the bed and gently retrieved a framed photo from the nightstand.

The old woman patted the bed beside her, and Victoria sat down carefully. They sat in silence for a few moments while the old woman gently ran her fingers over the chipped picture frame and deliberately traced the outline of the young girl in the photo.

Victoria looked around the room, which was several times larger than the tiny living area where the old woman had placed her things. Dozens of faded photographs hung on a nearby wall.

Still clutching the photo, the old woman finally spoke, "This is why I'm here; she's my daughter."

"What happened to her?" Victoria asked.

The old woman's body tensed, and a lone tear dripped down her cheek.

"She's lost, I guess. I mean, I haven't seen her in years. That's what I'm doing here; waiting."

She placed the photo back onto the nightstand and clasped her hands together. Victoria was puzzled; the hands looked familiar, yet she had never seen this woman.

Tears began to stream down the old woman's face. Victoria instinctively reached for the familiar hand, but the old woman pulled it away and gestured toward the photo wall.

"They don't understand," she said.

Victoria got up and moved to the wall, scanning the photos. Groups of people smiled and laughed, arms slung around each other. The old woman was much younger in the photos.

"Why are you waiting here alone? Why not go back and wait with them?" Victoria nodded toward the wall of photos where she was standing.

"Nobody understands how much I miss her. They want me to go on without her, but I can't; she's all I care about now."

The old woman began to sob. Suddenly a black cloud appeared from behind her. It swirled around her midsection, gaining speed as it covered more of her body. With each revolution, a tip of the black cloud stabbed at her chest, causing her to cry out in agony.

Victoria stepped backward until she was plastered against the photo wall. A picture crashed down, and the glass broke at her feet, but she never took her eyes off the old woman.

"What's happening?" Victoria shouted.

"Get out of here, now!" demanded the old woman.

"Wait, let me help you," Victoria pleaded.

"Leave me alone, please," cried the old woman.

Victoria stepped toward the black cloud that now enshrouded the old woman. Although she couldn't see her anymore, she could make out the outline of the old woman's body. Sobs came from somewhere inside the blackness.

"I want to be alone, please go now!" the old woman pleaded.

Victoria glanced at the hole in the wall on the far side of the cave and back at the screaming black cloud. Not sure what to do, she finally turned away from the old woman and ran toward the tunnel opening. Victoria bent down to exit the cave when a large mirror above the hole caught her attention.

Her heart was pounding, and she needed to get out of there... to find her way back home, but she was mesmerized by the mirror; its gold frame encrusted with precious stones.

She could hear the old woman's faint cries from the back of the cave.

Reaching out to touch the frame, Victoria was startled by her hand, the same hand she had noticed on the old woman. She stepped in front of the mirror and gasped. Staring back at her was the old woman.

### *The Forgotten Wall*

I was becoming the Old Woman in the Cave. It wasn't just that I missed my daughter every single day, but I was desperate to have her back. I couldn't seem to focus fully for any length of time on much else. I was distracted by memories, agonized over what may never be, and terrified of what was still to come.

The more I focused on Jordan, the sadder and lonelier I became. I lived with that imaginary black cloud over my heart, and it was getting darker by the day. I was retreating into my own cave, my self-imposed prison. The black cloud of depression was beginning to suffocate me.

The photos on my own wall were beginning to fade. If I didn't take drastic measures to re-focus, I too was going to have a wall of forgotten people. It is natural to focus on what we have lost, and we have every right to grieve, for a time. You enter the danger zone when you're singularly focused on the loss or pain for so long that it begins to interfere with or destroy your other relationships; the very relationships you need to help you out of your cave. You may end up with a Forgotten Wall of loved ones.

 **Are you in danger of becoming the old woman (or man) in the cave; how so?**

 **Who are the people that are in danger of ending up on your Forgotten Wall?**

## Focus Board

Our minds have the power to create images that can either help or hurt us. Since actions begin with thoughts, then what we think about is important. Visualization not only affects your attitude but in turn, your actions. Therefore, be careful to create the proper images in your mind. It will become nearly impossible to heal if the only images you allow into your mind are those that are at the center of your pain, your loss, your Beast.

You have the ability to think about whatever you want, so begin to recreate images that will inspire and support your victory over the Beast. First thing in the morning, give yourself time to focus and reflect on what you have; what you're thankful for. Say a prayer of thanksgiving and get your mind focused on the people and situations that will help you to move forward; to heal.

In the beginning stages of your re-focusing process, it will be tremendously helpful to create some tangible images that you can gravitate toward to help you to stay focused on the right things. Consider creating a Focus Board, which is a collage of images that serve as your visual reminders.

Perhaps you have created a vision or a goal board. A Focus Board is similar, but there is an important difference. The purpose of a vision or goal board is for you to visualize what you want to attract and achieve in your future. Some of the things on your Focus Board are indeed future-oriented, but a Focus Board is more about what needs and deserves your focus TODAY. To get to the future, you have to get through the day. A Focus Board can help. When I'm tempted to focus too much on Jordan or to head into fear mode, I re-focus on the people, places and things that are on my Focus Board. Here are some examples of images on my Focus Board:

- My family and extended family.
- My husband and son who are huge San Francisco 49er fans, at a game.
- Photos of me with Rich.
- My goddaughter and namesake. Her photo reminds me to be the woman her parents want their daughter to be like.
- Jordan, in happier times.
- A photo of a rainbow that I took in my backyard.
- My cat Shiska - he has been by my side through it all.
- Inspirational photographs, e.g., a photo of a little boy running on prosthetic legs, pure joy spread across his face, with the captions reading: "Your Excuse is Invalid."
- Mountains - the majesty inspires me, and I love hiking.
- Inspirational quotes and reminders.
- Some of the places I want to visit. Although this is more future centered, it reminds me now to keep my passion for travel and that my traveling days are not over.
- The Rockin' Redhead logo, which encourages me to stay focused on my mission of making meaning from the madness.
- A heart with the words: "I'm not afraid of the future because God is already there." It helps me to replace fear with faith.

- My great-niece. Her photo reminds me that although life is full of loss, it is also full of joy.

You get the idea. Glue images onto a poster board and have it laminated to keep everything secure.

Since I spend a great deal of time in my home office, I have mine on my office wall. If you work outside the home and have a space for it, place it on the wall there. If not, you could create a small photo album, a digital version to serve as a screen saver, or a series of images on your smartphone. Consider creating two Focus Boards; one for home and one for your place of work.

Whatever method you choose, be certain it is easily accessible and that you use it.

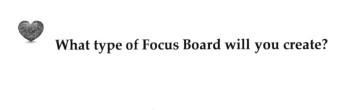 **What type of Focus Board will you create?**

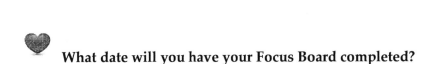 **Where will you keep it?**

 **What date will you have your Focus Board completed?**

## You Are More Than a _____

You are more than what you are going through, more than your Beast. When reality sunk in and I had to admit I was the mother of a heroin addict, it hurt. We put labels on people, and on situations. I didn't want the label - **mother of an addict**.

Whether or not people realize it, they judge you. There is a stigma attached to drug addiction and mental illness that also follows the families, especially the parents. I no longer allow myself to be defined by the stigma that is placed on me due to my daughter's disease.

At a time when I was missing Jordan, when the hole in my heart for her was so big that I could barely breathe, my sister-in-law wrote me this note. She reminded me I'm far more than the mother of an addict.

*Val,*

*You are my sister and my friend. You are energetic, bold, clever and beautiful. You are a daughter. You are supportive. You love the family and sacrifice to serve the family.*

*You are a wife. You are sexy, hard-headed, and loyal. Richie digs you. You are a mother. Fiercely protective, nurturing, and carry the history of your children's lives with you in your heart. You are the bow to their arrows, and your bow is strong and true. Sometimes arrows fly, unexpected, to places never intended. They may be lost for a time, until they are recovered. They may be scuffed and rusty, the feathers torn and tattered. But if returned to you, you would do your best to prepare them for flight again.*

*Lastly, you are Valerie. A little girl, with hopes and wild dreams that has grown into an impeccable woman who walks this earth with pride and pain, beauty and uncertainty, and a most contagious spirit.*

*I love you Val,*

*Suz*

You are more than a label. More than your child's addiction or your father's disgrace. You are more than your mistakes, the past, or your battle. You are strong, courageous and valuable. Your future is full of potential and possibility.

## Fitting the Pieces Together

When you **Adjust Your Focus** away from troubles, you will be in a better mindset to **Stand <u>On</u> Your Story** and **Make Meaning From the Madness.** If you are knocked down, keeping your focus will allow you to once again, **Decide to Stand Up and Fight.** Proper focus will give you the energy to **Get On Your Spiritual Armor** and **Put On Your Oxygen Mask**. Since you **Build Your Circle of Strength** with other people, your sole focus will no longer be on yourself or your Beast. The right focus is necessary to **Change Your Attitude** and to keep it positive. Until you're properly focused, it will be very difficult to **Stop Being a Control Freak.**

## Your Declaration

Complete the Adjust Your Focus declaration in order to commit to keeping your focus on the right people, situations, and events. As my sister-in-law reminded me that I am more than a mother, more than a mother of an addict, you too are much more than your Beast.

---

### Adjust Your Focus Declaration

I, _____ am in a battle with a Beast. My Beast is: _____

_____

Today, _____, 20_____ I am committed to adjusting my Focus to people and things that move my life forward in a positive and healthy direction. I will not become the Old Woman in the Cave. I declare that I am more than a:

_____. I am also:

_____

_____

_____

_____

_____
Signed

---

## Faith in the Battle

*"I lift up my eyes to the mountains-where does my help come from? My help comes from the Lord, the Maker of heaven and earth."* **Psalm 121:1-2**

While I am grateful for what social media has brought to our culture, it is not without its problems. In the age of selfies and Instagram, people can create an image of themselves that contradicts who they really are, but that doesn't seem to matter, as long as others believe the facade. When we are living with a Beast, we can only hide behind the selfies and videos we post of happier times for so long. At some point the label "Addict's Mom, Divorcee, High-School Drop-out, Unemployed, Mentally-Ill, Depressed, or a host of others" make their way into our image of ourselves. If we are not careful, we will be crushed under the weight of our own self-deprecation and society's stigma that we are broken and need to be fixed. It is a stigma that blames us for our messed-up kids or failed marriages as if the other parties in the relationship had no part in how things turned out at all. While this may seem slightly over-dramatized, it really isn't. Social media through its photo-shopped images smiling back at us has perpetuated this lie by convincing us that we really can have smart and successful children if we give them great educations and keep them away from negative influences. It convinces us if we work 24/7, we will have successful careers making beaucoup bucks. It also convinces us that if we are the perfect wife, our husbands will never leave us for a woman half our age. Why? Because people, in general, need a place to hide their shame, and it's usually under a nice blanket of finger-pointing and blame.

In **John 9:2**, the disciples asked Jesus regarding a man born blind, "Rabbi, who sinned, this man or his parents, that he was born blind?" It was customary in Jewish culture at the time to believe that blindness was the result of sin. Jesus answered in verse 3 that "neither this man nor his parents sinned." He went on to say, "but this happened so that the works of God might be displayed in him." Ouch! I would kind of like to ignore that verse! Even then people wanted assurance that if they did everything right, themselves and their families would not suffer. As Jesus pointed out, though, there is often a greater purpose in suffering, and we might possibly be able to see it if we learn to adjust our focus.

As Christians, our church is a place we usually go to find encouragement and support. While some churches have wonderful support groups for those who are suffering and their families, many are still dropping the ball. Sadly, I have spoken to leaders in churches who have tried to start support groups with no success. Perhaps this is because it is especially hard for us to feel safe enough to be transparent within the church community for fear of being judged or that our secret might get out. We turn inward for many reasons from pride to shame to feeling completely hopeless. For whatever reason, we are tempted to isolate ourselves and withdraw from the people in our lives who can give us the strength and encouragement we need to keep getting up each morning. We lose sight of the blessings and beauty all around us in our families and friends, in nature, in music, and in time spent just being rather than doing. By obsessing over our families and their problems and trying to fix them, or even our own personal battles with our Beasts, we develop tunnel vision. The world around us ceases to exist to us as our obsession takes us deeper into loneliness and isolation.

Valerie told a story of the Old Woman in the Cave and how she had fallen into this deep, dark hole. One thing that stood out to me was that she was cooking something that smelled dreadful on her pot-bellied stove. No doubt, she was stirring up a pot of self-pity and regret. On the cave wall, hung pictures of her with loved ones in happier times. Instead, she focused on the one she had lost. She stirred her self-pity soup and convinced herself she was all alone even with all the faces smiling back at her as she isolated herself in that cold, dark cave. She refused help even when it was staring her in the face because she had convinced herself that she was in a hopeless situation with the only way out being her daughter's safe return. Granted some of the people in those pictures may have turned away from her, but had she allowed them, many would have been there to lift her up and remind her that she is loved and precious to them. The Lord does that for us. He has a plan for us, and he wants us to see beyond our current circumstances, but first, we need to focus on him and what he wants for our lives.

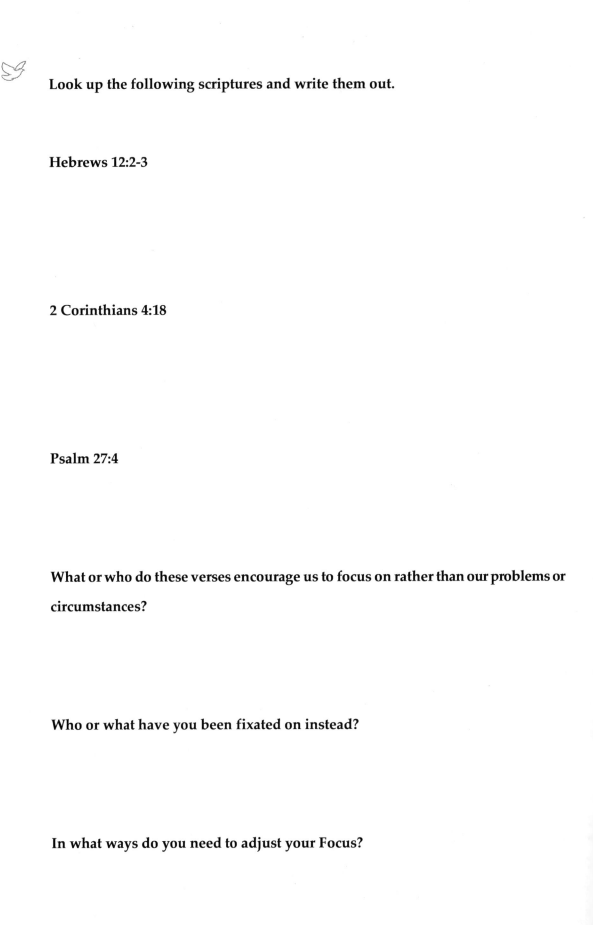

**Look up the following scriptures and write them out.**

**Hebrews 12:2-3**

**2 Corinthians 4:18**

**Psalm 27:4**

**What or who do these verses encourage us to focus on rather than our problems or circumstances?**

**Who or what have you been fixated on instead?**

**In what ways do you need to adjust your Focus?**

**In what ways do you need to adjust your focus? What or who have you been looking at instead of Jesus and his promises?**

In my case, I was focused on fighting my son's addiction Beast and fixing his problems. I finally realized I was wasting (yes, I do mean wasting) far too much time researching addiction treatment options, reading articles about the treatment of drug addiction in our country, and even going on social media sites that were much more focused on the problem instead of the solution. The reason I say wasted is that I was doing the work my son should have been doing for himself. I wish I had a dollar for every hour I spent trying to solve his problems; instead, I accomplished nothing except to feel more hopeless than before. While I understand that research and information are valuable and necessary for recovery, an over-emphasis on time spent focusing on his addiction, especially when he did not want the help, took precious attention away from my family and friends who also needed me. Like me, many of you may find yourself like the Old Woman in the Cave, obsessing over whoever or whatever you have lost. All this obsessing won't change a thing except to make you more isolated and withdrawn. Perhaps it is time to step out of your cave, visit your Forgotten Wall, and embrace the loved ones you may have left behind while you were in there.

*"I sought the Lord, and he answered me; he delivered me from all my fears."* **Psalm 34:4**

Along with a Focus Board, why not consider a gratitude journal or jar? An attitude of gratitude and thanksgiving can go a long way in stimulating hope in our hearts. In that journal, you can place memories of times when God brought you through difficult trials or something you are grateful for today. It can be something as simple as being thankful for pancakes and syrup to something as challenging as surviving a life-threatening illness. As I started writing in my gratitude journal, I realized that I had forgotten many times how the Lord showed himself to be faithful in even the smallest details of my life. Perhaps as you start your journal, you can make it a goal to write down a few things each day you are thankful for, as well as memories that you are grateful for.

**What do the following verses say about being thankful?**

**1 Thessalonians 5:18**

**Psalm 9:1**

**Ephesians 5:20**

What would it look like and sound like if you could go an entire day without verbalizing fear, doubt, worry, or complaining? What would be the things you would say if you truly believed nothing was impossible for God? How would you pray today if you knew your prayers were guaranteed answered favorably? I know we don't always get the answers we want in this lifetime, but as we adjust our focus and walk in an attitude of gratitude, our faith will start to grow again.

In this last section, take a few minutes to write in your gratitude journal your hopes and dreams of how you would like to see the Lord move in your life. Take as much time and use as much paper as you need for this assignment. Remember, no fear or doubt can be journaled in this entry. When you are done with your entry, go back and read through it again. How does it make you feel? Has adjusting your focus helped to change your attitude towards yourself, others, and your situation?

Finally, read Proverbs 31:25-30 and ask the Lord to let you see yourself through his eyes. Be brave and write his description of you verbatim. Are you able to see yourself differently as you consider how the Lord sees you? Are you ready to replace the old labels with some new ones? If so, adjust your focus and enjoy the compliments!

*"Hope is the thing with feathers*
*That perches in the soul*
*And sings the tune without the words*
*And never stops at all."*
**-Emily Dickenson**

## *Action #7: Stop Being a Control Freak*

"It is said that the definition of insanity is: doing the same thing over and over and expecting a different result. My definition of insanity is: **trying to change something or someone that you cannot change.**"

— **Valerie Silveira**

## Action Introduction

For the longest time, I thought my influence over Jordan would be enough to make her change. After she had been shot, I was certain my love and encouragement would remind her of who she was. Once she was deep into her addiction, I still thought that there was something I could say that would make a difference. I searched for the perfect phrase, scripture, or words of wisdom. I thought I could find the right thing to say or do that would turn on the lightbulb in her brain, and it would be the moment everything began to turn around for Jordan, for me. I said and did anything and everything I could think of to try to make her change; to return to my Jordan, whom I was longing to have back. I finally had to realize Jordan's addiction is one of the things I cannot change.

### *The Serenity Prayer*

*"God, grant me the serenity to accept the things I cannot change, the courage to change the things I can, and the wisdom to know the difference."*

*— Unknown*

The Serenity Prayer is a prayer for everyone, a mantra for which we should all strive. I have constantly prayed for the serenity to accept the things I cannot change. I have prayed for the courage to change myself in the middle of the worst period of my life. It's the third part of this prayer that might be the most challenging - the wisdom to know the difference. The difference between what we can change and what we cannot.

Incredible amounts of energy go into failed attempts at changing a situation you don't have the power to change; the same energy that could be used to change something you can. You can change your attitude, focus, relationships, and faith. You can change your fitness, how much you forgive, and how you think. You can change the way you speak to and about others, and the way you speak to yourself. The bottom line is that the only person you can change is you.

It is said the definition of insanity is: doing the same thing over and over and expecting a different result. **My definition of insanity is, trying to change something or someone you can't change.**

The real power is in letting go of what you cannot change and working on what you can. Pray for, and work toward gaining the wisdom to know the difference between the things you cannot change and the things you can.

 **Have you expended effort trying to change someone or something you cannot change? Who is it and what have you been doing?**

## The "F" Word Will Set You Free

Start using the "F" word. If you have been living with or battling a Beast, you really need the "F" word. Not that "F" word, although you may have used that one too a few times. The "F" word I am referring to is Forgiveness.

> *"Forgiveness is unlocking the door to set someone free and realizing you were the prisoner."*
> —*Max Lucado*

Forgiving may be one of the biggest obstacles you come up against, and once you learn to do it often, it will be one of the most powerful things you ever do. Forgiving another person for an offense can seem as if we are excusing the behavior, so we choose not to forgive. Instead, we become angry, resentful and bitter. Holding onto anger and resentment rarely results in hurting or changing another person. We only hurt ourselves.

## Start Using the "F" Word All the Time

When The Guy shot my daughter in 2004, I wanted him to suffer. *I . . . wanted . . . him . . . to . . . suffer!* I was the mama bear, and my cub had nearly been killed. I was hurt and scared. I wanted him to pay for what he did, and I carried that anger around for a long time, even after he was convicted and sent to prison.

According to the law, The Guy *was* paying for what he did, but that wasn't good enough for me. Jordan had changed, and I blamed him. For the three years leading up to the shooting, Jordan had made terrible decisions, some having nothing to do with The Guy. It didn't matter, I wanted and needed to blame someone other than Jordan, and The Guy was the obvious choice.

The Guy had no idea how angry I was with him or whether or not I had forgiven him. If he had known, he probably wouldn't have cared. Who was I punishing? Me.

The Guy was not the only one in prison. I was locked up in my self-imposed prison of unforgiveness. Once I came to that realization, I opened the prison door, and slowly set myself free.

Expending energy holding onto anger is foolish. When you're battling a Beast, you will need all of your energy focused in the right direction. Don't waste any of it living with anger and resentment as a result of your unwillingness to forgive.

 **Do you understand and agree that not forgiving someone is holding you back; that it is like a self-imposed prison?**

**Are you willing to open the prison doors and set yourself free?**

## Give Yourself a Pardon

The "F" word may be harder to say to yourself than it is to say to others, even people who have hurt you deeply. Sometimes the difficulty lies in the uncertainty of why you need to forgive yourself. It may be that you are attempting to blame yourself unnecessarily.

For the better part of thirteen years, I picked myself apart, in an attempt to pinpoint the cause of Jordan's behavior, and eventually, her addiction. Separating me from my child proved nearly impossible. I was a single parent for many of Jordan's formidable years, and, therefore, concluded there must have been something I did or didn't do that caused Jordan's disease. It had to be my fault she jumped onto her Roller Coaster From Hell.

At the very least, I had to be a contributor. It didn't matter that Jordan didn't blame me, or that my family and friends told me I was a great mother. Nothing anyone said could keep me from the mental and emotional abuse I piled on myself.

It proved much easier for me to even forgive Jordan for her choices than it was for me to forgive myself for something I had yet to figure out. Mama and papa bears find it much simpler to point the finger at themselves than at their cubs. When teenagers and adult children cause a mother terrible pain and heartbreak, she will give herself whiplash turning the other cheek. Wives will forgive abusive husbands until they are blue (or black) in the face. Granting self-forgiveness can be very difficult.

You may have made some very bad choices in the past. Maybe you have caused the people you love a great deal of pain. If you have already asked the people you have hurt for forgiveness but are continuing to withhold forgiveness from yourself, then you're choosing the prison of unforgiveness.

We have all made mistakes. There are plenty of choices I have made, things I have said, or actions I have taken for which I am not proud. Most people will tell you if they had it to do over, they would do things the same way. I wonder if that is true. I would go back and do many things very differently.

Whether you would choose to change the past or not, you can't. You can't change a single second of the past, but you can choose to forgive yourself. Until you can find a way to forgive yourself, it will be difficult for you to truly forgive anybody else.

In our attempts to control a very out-of-control situation, we attempt to control others. Maybe not the direct actions or behaviors of others, but sometimes we try to control what others think or feel.

I was caught in between what I assumed people thought or felt about Jordan and how I felt about her. Since I was enabling her and trying to control her behavior, I remained convinced she was going to turn the corner at any moment and my family would be whole again. Therefore, I wanted to be sure when she did, she would be welcomed back with open arms by everyone.

It's not easy to separate ourselves from our families and especially our children. We believe they are a reflection of their upbringing and therefore of us. If the apple doesn't fall far from the tree, how could Jordan be in another orchard?

When someone goes off the rails, we are all guilty of jumping to conclusions about their family. Everyone is curious about the parents of a school shooter or a serial killer. After an unimaginable event, it's natural to look for answers in an attempt to reconcile what has happened, and the entire family ends up under a microscope.

It isn't much different with addicts. People want to find an easy answer as to why the addiction manifested, whose DNA it came from, or what happened to cause the addiction. We go looking for answers, and the first stop is the family. In certain cases, family actions could have a great deal to do with how a child turns out or whether or not they wind up addicted to drugs or alcohol.

Many addicts or people who make very bad choices come from good homes. Unfortunately, people continue to jump to conclusions without understanding the complicated disease of addiction or other factors. I had jumped to those same conclusions many times before I had an addicted child.

It hurts when a family member acts in ways that are opposed to your values or expectations. You have a connection to your loved ones, so when they do something dishonest, or worse, there is a part of you that feels a certain sense of responsibility. Every fiber of your being becomes defensive, even if you're sickened by their actions. It feels like a direct hit when a negative comment or feeling has been launched at your child.

The actions of your family members, even your children, are not your actions. People may judge you because of the actions of your child, husband, brother, mother, aunt, or another family member. There is nothing you can do about it, so let them play judge and jury. Just as we can't control the behavior of our loved ones, we can't control the thoughts or feelings that other people have about those loved ones.

It may be that you are assuming people are more judgmental than they are, or that they are thinking about you far more than they are. When my children were overly concerned about what others were thinking, I would tell them:

**"Don't spend so much time thinking about what others are thinking about you. They don't spend nearly as much time thinking about you, as you do thinking about them thinking about you."**

The amount of self-contempt, judgment, and guilt you pile on yourself may be more than what anyone else will send your way. In any case, let it go.

 **Is it possible that your lack of self-forgiveness is tied to a perception that you or others may have toward you? For example, my perception was that no matter how old my daughter was, I was still somehow responsible for her addiction and her choices.**

If you have done something for which you feel guilty, it is still time to let it go; to forgive

yourself. If not, then skip the next question.

 **If you need to make amends with someone, who is it and what do you need to**

**deal with?**

 **Complete the following:**

I, _____ forgive myself for,

_____

_____

_____

_____

**I realize that I am not perfect, and that I have made mistakes. I recognize that I have placed more guilt on myself than was necessary, and that this guilt is eating away at me.**

**On this day, the _____ day of _____ , 20_____ , I hereby forgive myself, not only for this, but for anything and everything. I choose to go forward today with the burden of self-imposed guilt and shame removed from me. Today, I am free.**

_____

**Signed**

### "F" Them

The day I got the call informing me The Guy was released from the county jail and into the hands of the state correctional system, I didn't react the way I had thought I would. I didn't throw my arms up and cheer. I never had the party I claimed I was going to throw. Instead, I bawled like a baby.

I held my face in my hands and pictured The Guy. I saw him in a prison jumpsuit, with hands and ankles shackled; acting tough as fear took over every fiber of his being. It overwhelmed me to think about the once innocent baby whose life path brought him to a state of mind where he would abuse girls and fire a gun into a house full of people. Nineteen years after the innocent baby entered the world, he was headed to a state penitentiary.

Instead of feeling vindicated, I wept for the situation, and I forgave The Guy. Then I took it back.

### Use the "F" Word Over and Over

*"When asked how many times a brother should be forgiven for sinning against Him, Jesus replied, I don't say to you seven times but seventy-seven times."*
— **Matthew 18:21-22**

Even after you forgive someone, something might trigger an old feeling, and like I did with The Guy, you will snatch your forgiveness back as quickly as you gave it.

Forgiveness lightens the load you're carrying, so resist the urge to grab it back after you have given it away. If you keep taking back the forgiveness you have let go of and piling it back onto your own shoulders, before long, you have a new thousand-pound Beast on your shoulders.

There is no expiration date on forgiveness, so just keep at it. The important thing is to keep forgiving until you have nothing left to forgive.

### Forgiving the Source of Your Pain

It took me some time to forgive Jordan. I now understand she has a disease, but my frustration over her reluctance to treat her disease left me, among so many other emotions, angry. When someone has a disease affecting another part of the body, they get treatment. People take insulin, heart medication and use a whole host of other options to treat diseases. With drug addiction, the disease seems to repel treatment, making it harder for the patient to seek help.

Drug addiction is a Beast, a very large one. I hate drug addiction. I hate Jordan's Beast, but I love Jordan, so I had a hard time separating the two. My reluctance to forgive her was the age-old concern that forgiveness somehow excuses or justifies the behavior. I had no intention of forgiving the drug addiction Beast; why should I?

The answer is simple; Jordan's Beast is part of her, and therefore I had to forgive the whole thing. I forgave her for the lies, deceit, and for her unwillingness to fight. I forgave her for bringing danger and violence into our lives. I forgave her for wasting our money, ruining holidays and birthdays, and breaking my heart over and over again. I forgave her for tearing apart the thing I so desperately wanted back together - my family. I forgave her for all of it.

If I didn't forgive Jordan's drug addiction Beast, I couldn't have completely forgiven her. Had I not been able to forgive her, it would have been much more difficult to forgive myself.

Forgiving something as big and evil as Jordan's Beast, made it easier for me to forgive myself and to forgive others. Let go of anger and resentment. Whether or not another party is guilty, be generous with forgiveness, and it will pave the way for much healing. Believe it or not, forgiving your Beast may be a stepping-stone to removing him from your life.

Recognize the absolute necessity to forgive. Forgiveness is for you; let God deal with others. Let them deal with themselves. Let the justice system deal with them. Let their journey take them where it needs to take them. Use the "F" Word!

 **Are you ready to forgive those that you have been holding forgiveness from?**

 **If you are able, and can communicate with the person whom you want to forgive, then do so.**

 **Say a prayer for forgiveness and let it go.**

## It's Not All About You

Parents feel a certain degree of responsibility for their child's actions, even after those children are adults. Not only did I gladly strap on my Supermom Cape repeatedly, but I felt it was my duty. You may have similar thoughts and feelings about a spouse, parent or another loved one.

A few of my friends feel as if their ex-husband's new wives have benefitted at their expense. They will say, "It's not fair she gets him after I'm the one who went through all of the crap that made him a better husband!" It probably isn't fair if one chooses to look at it in that way.

Our part in another person's journey can be significant in allowing that person to mature, or grow. There should be some peace in knowing you had a hand in helping another person in their learning process. It is little solace when the wounds are fresh, but over time, it is important to find your way there.

As painful as your experience may have been, it does provide you an opportunity to learn and grow. I sacrificed a great deal attempting to help Jordan, so naturally, I wanted to be the person standing next to her when she finds her way. It isn't just that I sacrificed and tried to help; after all, I wasn't the only person who helped Jordan, but she is my daughter.

If Jordan finds a way to beat her Beast and one day stands in victory over it, I may not be the one standing with her, but does it really matter?

Whether or not you are the sacrificial lamb in somebody else's journey, in the end, it's their journey. It may hurt to hear this, but another person's journey is not about you, just as Jordan's is not about me.

 **Were you a catalyst for change or growth in another person's life? Who are they and what was the change or growth they experienced or may experience in the future?**

Can you find a way to let go of the fact that you might not be there to reap the benefit of your hard work in that person's life?

 Work to find satisfaction in knowing that you had an important place in their journey and that without you, they may not get to where they need to go.

 What have you learned from the experience?

## Excruciatingly Painful Love

If you run into a bear, you are in trouble. If you run into a mama bear with her cubs, you are dead.

When Sean was in fifth grade, the school had a lockdown. It had been reported that a man with a shotgun was seen near the playground of the school. Once the lockdown was over, I picked up Sean and a couple of his friends and drove them to our home.

We lived a mile or so from the school in a neighborhood just off the main road that divided several housing developments. Between the main road and our back yard was a greenbelt. After an event such as a school lockdown, adrenalin is running high, to say the least. It didn't take long for my overactive mind to convince myself the gunman had evaded capture by hiding in the greenbelt.

Driving up our street, I conjured up visions of the mad gun-toting man hiding in our house. My heart raced as I grabbed a golf club from the garage and charged into the house. I went room to room, golf club in the air, daring this imaginary intruder to mess with me.

By the time I made it downstairs, Sean and his friends were behind me laughing. I seriously don't know what I would have done had an intruder jumped out at me from behind a shower curtain pointing a shotgun at me. What I do know is that I felt powerful and fearless because I was protecting my cub, and his friends.

The majority of moms are not much different from a mama bear. Mess with me and you might have trouble, but don't mess with my kids. We are incredibly protective of our children. There was no doubt in my mind I would have protected my son, at the potential cost of my life.

Dealing with hardships, heartbreak, loss and pain is a battle. When the person responsible for causing your pain is your child, you can become paralyzed. We are wired to provide for and protect our children. When they are in trouble, we are the mama bear (or daddy bear) fiercely fighting for our cubs.

What do you do when you raise your weapon to defend your child, and it is the child staring back at you?

When we make tough parenting decisions, it is called tough love. Walking away from a child who is on a freight train headed for a brick wall isn't tough, it is excruciating.

Tough love is not allowing your child to go to the movies on Friday night. Taking a stand with a child is not easy, which is why it is called "tough love." Pulling out the safety net and allowing my only daughter to crash has not been tough, it has been excruciating. I call it excruciatingly painful love.

Letting Jordan fall is without question, one of the hardest things I have ever done, but also the right thing. A few years back Jordan screamed, "It's my life!" She was right; it is her life. Unfortunately, though, her life choices have an impact on a lot of other people. Each person is responsible for their choices, for who they become. Although your journey is uniquely yours, it's important to remember how interwoven your life is with others' lives.

I feared if I turned away from Jordan, she might forget how much I love her. She may think she has nobody left and, therefore, give up. I shared that sentiment with my friend, Teresa, whose daughter has been in a battle with a drug addiction Beast. Teresa sent me this text:

*"Sweetheart, you have proven and proven and proven... did I say proven...your love for your girl; unconditional, not based on her behavior or merit. She knows this, and she may call you a bitch when you resist her attempts to control you, but deep down in her 'knower,' she has been loved by you as only a mother can love, and that is all truth that even in the height of selfishness she can't deny."*

People, especially addicts, who have been using us for a long time, can make us feel obligated to continue in the Cycle of Hope and Disappointment. As my friend Teresa said, deep down in their "knower," they know you love them and have been there for them more than what should have been expected. There is no need for you to prove it over and over again.

## If It Were Possible, It Would Be Done

Are you exhausting yourself in an effort to save someone from themselves? I was desperate to save my daughter from herself - to battle her drug Beast for her. Jordan told me what I wanted to hear. Things were always going to change *in a couple of weeks*. Drug addicts lie to keep you in the game - the enabling game. She strung me along, took advantage of my generosity and my love. She is smart and knew how to get me to keep believing the lies, or at least wanting to believe them. Ultimately, it was my choice to keep believing her Beast.

The reality that hit me one day was this: **If it were possible for me to save Jordan from herself, I would have done it long ago!**

If all it took was effort, money, tears, sleepless nights, and love…it would have been over years ago. It was then that I took a step back and surveyed the situation. No matter that my heart had been shattered into a million pieces. I could allow it to be shattered into a million and one pieces, and the situation would remain the same. The harsh reality is that I can't save my daughter; she has to save herself.

You cannot save someone either. Your loved ones have choices, but so do you.

 **If it was possible to save someone, would you have already done it?**

## Taking Off the Cape

Love is the reason you strap on your Supermom or Super_____ (fill in the blank) Cape in the first place, but fear is what keeps it tied around your neck. You want to be ready at all times, just in case your loved one needs you. If your loved one is involved in self-destructive behavior, the chances are you will use it so often you may as well leave it on.

It was time; I knew I needed to take off my Supermom Cape. Deep down, I knew my enabling disguised as helping, was not helping Jordan. By the time I realized it, the Cape had been on for years, and there was a big knot in it, which would require some effort to remove it. I took out the scissors, but I couldn't get my hands to work. My head knew it was the right thing to do, but my heart was in control of the scissors.

I finally got my heart in agreement with my head and made the cut. I did it for me, and for Jordan. She needs to find her own way, and I was tired of riding the Roller Coaster from Hell. The Cape was so worn out there was nothing much left of it. I ran my fingers over the rips and tears and poked my fingers through the holes. I gently stroked the tattered edges and folded it up neatly.

Then panic set in, what if I needed it again? I didn't trust myself, so I gave the Cape to Rich, for safe keeping. He probably burned it. I came clean with my husband and stopped hiding my enabling and codependent behavior from him.

Depending on how long you have worn your Cape, it may feel strange once you take it off. When I took mine off, it felt as if a part of me was missing. I had worn that Cape for more than a decade. A part of me was missing, but an even bigger part of me was free. I was no longer a party to Jordan's drug addiction.

A mom of an addict wrote to me about her daughter:

> *"She has told me repeatedly that she doesn't have an addiction. I have thought maybe I should try to get help, do more for her. Then I think, who am I kidding? I have tried that. So, it's time to enjoy all the wonderful blessings in my life, turn her over to God and on with life. I also realized that she is not ready for help yet. I'm ready for help and healing; that's what I have to focus on."*

If you are wearing a Cape in an effort to save another person, take out the scissors and cut the string that binds you to your Cape. If you don't, not only will you practically hang yourself with the Cape, you will continue to prevent your loved one from learning what they need to learn. Understand you had good intentions, and forgive yourself if you wore it far too long.

 **What is holding you back from taking off the Cape?**

 **Has your coming to this person's rescue time and again, made a long-term positive impact?**

It is more likely your actions have had a negative impact. What are the negative impacts?

 How has wearing the Cape held you back?

 When are you going to take it off?

### Fitting the Pieces Together

It is not easy to **Stop Being a Control Freak. You** will most certainly need the other Actions to support your efforts, just as you will need to let go of control in order to successfully implement the other Actions. You will need to loosen your grip enough to allow yourself to **Decide to Stand Up and Fight** and to **Get On Your Spiritual Armor.** When you attempt to control things you can't control you will exhaust yourself before you have a chance to **Put On Your Oxygen Mask.** In order to **Build Your Circle of Strength,** you will need to place your trust in others, which is impossible to do when you are trying to control everything. Being a control freak will affect your ability to **Change Your Attitude** and to **Adjust Your Focus.** How will you **Stand <u>On</u> Your Story** and **Make Meaning From the Madness** if you don't allow yourself to be vulnerable, to learn and to grow?

## Your Declaration

Fill in the blanks of the Stop Being a Control Freak declaration. Today is the day that you commit to stop trying to control the uncontrollable.

**Stop Being a Control Freak Declaration**

I, _____ am in a battle with a Beast. My Beast is: _____

_____

Today, _____, 20_____ I will stop trying to control the uncontrollable. If my actions are not truly helping myself or others, I will take of my Super_____ Cape. I will use the "F" work as much as possible, and especially on myself. I declare that I will start living with more power, by letting go of things I never had control over in the first place.

_____
Signed

## Faith in the Battle

I call my Beast the "Triple Header" with Control Freak being the leader of the pack. My Codependent and Enabler Beasts are merely in existence to do the Control Freak Beast's bidding. Now to my defense, I am an adult child of an alcoholic and the oldest child of three children, so I grew up with an over-inflated sense of responsibility. Combine that with a Type-A, take-charge personality and verbal skills that could out-argue the most experienced litigator around, and Control Freak had found its perfect host. My role in the family was that of maintaining the temperature of the household. If things got a little heated with my dad, I would try and cool things down by making peace as the family mediator. If my mom was angry and upset, which was often, she was as cold as ice so I would try to warm things up by doing something nice for her. I had two younger siblings, my sister, two years younger than me, and my brother, who was seven years younger. Because he was the baby of the family, I adopted him as my own, and I was definitely responsible for him, from changing his diapers to seeing to it that he was bathed and fed.

Once married, I was no different. I constantly fought for control in our marriage, but thank goodness, my husband is not one to be pushed around. He has a quiet will of iron and is not easily manipulated by my nagging or pleading. So, if I can't control him, I might as well control my children, right? Having children gives us a false sense that we have some sort of control in their lives. While they were young, we chose what they would eat and wear, what schools they would attend, and what friends they would play with. As they grew, we had less control over those influences and the decisions they made. In reality, we never had any real control. For example, think about if you were the President or Vice-President of a corporation. While you may have responsibility for many hundreds, even thousands of employees, you still answer to the owner of the company. It is his company, they are his employees, and he has the final say in everything. In life, we are often reminded of how little control, if any, we have of the people in our lives and the choices they make.

Whether that person we seek to control is a child, a spouse, a parent, a friend, or even a boss, and in spite of their actions, God is always in control, so we don't have to be.

### *The Serenity Prayer*

*"God, grant me the serenity to accept the things I cannot change, the courage to change the things I can, and the wisdom to know the difference."*

-Unknown

Valerie wrote earlier in this chapter about what she considers to be the most challenging part of the serenity prayer-the wisdom to know the difference. I could not agree with her more. I often struggle with knowing when to take action by being active and when to take action by doing nothing. Yes, doing nothing is an action and sometimes doing nothing is much harder than charging in to save the day. I am reminded of the time my mother told me about a conversation she had with my son regarding me. He was talking to her about how he feels I always need to be right. My mom wisely reminded him that I have only his safety and best interest in mind. She also asked him a very pointed question. "Can you give me an example of when your mom was wrong about you and why you felt she was wrong?" He answered, "No! But why does she always "have" to be right?!!" While I may have been right about what I said to him, I was wrong about when and how I said it or if it should have been said at all. At times, I took action when it may have been best to simply leave things alone. I had not accepted the things I could not change and felt I had to speak my mind. In doing so, I pushed him even further away, and he had tuned me out a long time ago. Knowing when to speak and when to listen, when to act and when not to, that is the wisdom to know the difference.

 **Look up the following verses and note what they tell us about wisdom.**

**Job 12:13**


**Proverbs 1:7**


**James 1:5**


Wisdom means "knowledge with discernment" and in my case, having it was imperative because my son was controlled by an addiction Beast.   A person under its control will lie, cheat, steal, and pretty much do anything else to get their next fix.  It is impossible to relate in any way, shape, or form to what is going on in their heads and what they are capable of. No matter what Beast we are living with, I think it's fair to say it can be very confusing and overwhelming knowing what to do and what not to do in any given situation. Before we take any action at all, we need to understand that knowledge is important, but wisdom is mandatory.  Wisdom takes into account past experiences, gut instincts, our awareness of who that person is in their soul, relational dynamics, and most importantly, the ability to be led by the Spirit of God as He speaks into our lives and directs our steps. His wisdom instructs us when to walk away and when to move forward.  It shows us the right thing to do or say at exactly the right time. We can trust in God's wisdom, but to hear from Him, we must first relinquish any false sense of control we might still be holding onto. Wisdom motivates us to willingly surrender and ask God to move in the situation as He sees best.  When we no longer look through the smoke and mirrors of a false sense of control, we are better equipped to get out of the driver's seat and let God take the wheel.

*"Do not conform to the pattern of this world, but be transformed by the renewing of your mind. Then you will be able to test and approve what God's will is-his good, pleasing and perfect will."*

**Romans 12:2**

There are many old thought and behavior patterns we will have to change once we decide to stop being a Control Freak. One of the most important areas we will need to change will be in how we choose to respond to hurts and disappointments caused by others or even by our own wrong actions. When someone has hurt or disappointed us in an unexpected or deeply painful way, especially when that hurtful behavior continues with no sign of change or remorse, we can become stuck, not knowing what to do next. We may even question the validity of the relationship or if it is worth trying to repair. We find ourselves at a critical fork in the road, a place where we can either choose to move forward towards freedom or where we stay stuck, licking our wounds and replaying the painful scenario until all the good in that relationship has been replaced with only bitterness. The gate we must step through to continue on our journey to freedom is that of forgiveness, the "F" word, as Valerie calls it. According to Strong's concordance to forgive means: "to release, dismiss, pardon, a sending away, a letting go, freedom." At this gate, we have the choice to let go of our own guilt and self-blame for being less than perfect. Here we confess to God the choices we made as we have tried to steer our own course, believing he needed our help to fix the people in our lives. On this path, we also release others to pave their own journeys whether they ask for or even deserve our forgiveness.

In **Luke 23:34**, Jesus prayed, "Father, forgive them, for they do not know what they are doing." His last public act prior to his death was to pray for our forgiveness, and through his death, we were reunited with God, our Father. This is really big stuff. There is life and freedom in forgiveness. Without it, we are held prisoners to our past hurts and are unable to move forward into freedom no matter how hard we try. Forgiveness is the key that unlocks the door to our hearts and allows love to flow freely again. As you read the following scriptures, ask yourself the question, "Who do I need to forgive?" Perhaps you are holding onto unforgiveness against your son or daughter, your spouse, a parent, yourself, a friend who hurt you, or even God? As you search these scriptures, ask the Lord to reveal the hidden closet where you keep your secret resentments and hurts and make you aware of any unforgiveness you have tucked away in there.

 **Look up the following verses and note what they say regarding forgiveness.**

**Matthew 6:14-15**

**Ephesians 4:32**

**Colossians 3:13**

You may be saying to yourself right about now, "I just do not know how to forgive them for what they have done to me!" Forgiveness comes as the Spirit of Christ works within us to love. To truly forgive someone who has hurt us, we will first need to examine the condition of our own hearts and how much God has forgiven us.

**Luke 6:41** reads, "Why do you look at the speck of sawdust in your brother's eye and pay no attention to the plank in your own?" I always picture a huge tree sticking out of not just my eye, but my entire head, and me with a tiny pair of tweezers trying to pick a little sliver out of someone's eye. I am twisting and turning trying to get the right angle to get a better view and in the process demolishing everything in sight! If and only when I get the speck out of their eye, do I turn around and look at the destruction left behind. Another job well done! It's a hysterical image! To avoid causing more harm than good, we need to first start with self-examination. Daily we should in humility seek God in prayer, seeking his forgiveness, and then, in turn, forgive others for even the seemingly smallest wrongs.

 **Look up and write out Matthew 6:12:**

The Lord's prayer guides us in how to approach God in prayer. At first, it seems quite simple in its content, but it is powerful in its purpose. It makes us painfully aware of our own failures as we come to him seeking forgiveness. It teaches that we pray for him to forgive us (present tense) as we also have forgiven others (past tense). Here is the key and we can't miss it. To receive forgiveness, we must be willing to give it. We are empowered to forgive as we let the Lord's infinite love flow in us and through us. **1 Peter 4:8** reassures us that, "love covers a multitude of sins." Love covers the hurt brought against us, allowing us to truly forgive the one who caused it.

Valerie wrote earlier of her need to cut off her Supermom Cape. Mine had to go also, and it was not going to be stored away for safe keeping. I was going to have to burn that baby! Perhaps you also have a Supermom Cape. Or maybe it's a Super-Wife Cape or a Super-Daughter Cape. Maybe it's a Super-I Can Do It All By Myself Cape. Whatever that Control Freak Cape is you are wearing, it's time to remove it, and it's not going to be easy.

There are many excuses for why we don't make the cut. We may be afraid, not ready or we might not believe it is the right action to take. We may have convinced ourselves that without our help, that person we are trying to save will crash. After all, in our opinion, their own ability to rid themselves of their Beasts failed a long time ago. While subtle, this belief can be a form of pride, and if we are not careful, it will permanently keep the cape strings tied tightly around our necks. Pride can come in the form of believing that we have the power to save them, but it can also hide behind an attitude of guilt that says, "if I had only been a better mother, daughter, wife, employee..."

Personally, I always cringe when I hear someone say to another parent whose kid turned out great, "You must be so proud of him. You did such a good job raising him." Perhaps, if spoken freely, they might say to me, "You must be so ashamed of yourself. You did such a lousy job raising him." Most people would not dare say those words out loud, but quite possibly, they might think them. I know I have said them to the image looking back at me in the mirror more times than I can count. What words are you letting your Beast accuse you of as it looks back at you in the mirror? In contrast, the opposite of pride is humility. Humility acknowledges that we have no control over another person's choices. Humility is the gateway for God's grace to guide us through that excruciatingly painful process of letting go. As we embrace grace, we embrace God's "unmerited favor" that gently loosens the hold that our need to control has held on us. We don't have to do it alone. God promises by his grace to help us every step of the way.

**Look up the following scriptures in the book of James and write them out:**

**James 4:6**

**James 4:10**

**Hebrews 4:6**

**Go back and review Valerie's questions pertaining to what might be holding you back from taking off your Super _____ Cape. Have any of your answers changed after reading these scriptures? If so, why?**

**Take a few minutes to write a prayer to God asking Him to help you forgive whoever it is who has caused you pain (perhaps it is yourself) and let go in love. Perhaps, write a letter to that person to offer forgiveness or ask for it, if necessary.**

*"I can rest in the fact that God is in control. Which means I can face things that are out of my control and not act out of control."-* **Lysa TerKeurst**

## *Action #8: Stand On Your Story*

*"Resist the temptation to wallow in self-pity, shame, guilt*

*or fear. Fight the urge to give up. Reject the notion that you*

*have become your story. Refuse to stay down on the mat.*

*Find the courage to stand up and become more, not in spite*

*of your story, but because of it."*


— ***Valerie Silveira***

## Action Introduction

When you experience a sudden tragedy or an ongoing agony, you will change. I am not the same person I was before all hell broke loose. Two decades ago, when Jordan was still innocent, and I had nothing but hope for the future, for her future, I was different than I am today. You are different than you were before all hell broke loose in your life.

Your life's two-by-four has changed you; living with a Beast has challenged you in ways you could not have imagined. Life experiences change us. It is up to us to decide what they will change us into.

Your Battle will also change you, and it can change you in positive ways that may be hard to see right now. I would be lying if I said I was glad things have happened the way they have. I'm not thankful Jordan slipped away, was shot, or became a drug addict. If it were possible, I would rewind the clock and change my story in a heartbeat. You probably wish you could turn your clock back too.

Since turning back the clock is not possible, we must own what has happened without shame or guilt. You need not stand in the muck of your story, like a victim after a storm. Stand up tall, put your shoulders back and declare that you are going to become a better person, not in spite of your story, but because of your story.

Resist the temptation to wallow in self-pity, shame, guilt or fear. Fight the urge to give up, or to give in. Reject the notion that you have become your story. Refuse to stay down on the mat. Shake off the stigma that society has thrown at you. Dig down and find the courage to become the person you would not have become had you not been a part of your own life's story.

## One Day At a Time

A mantra used by Alcoholics Anonymous and Narcotics Anonymous is: "One Day at a Time." This is good advice not only for someone in recovery, but it is great advice for everyone to live by. It's especially important to live by this philosophy when dealing with a Beast. Your battle may seem overwhelming, so projecting too far into the future can paralyze your progress.

Jesus said, "Do not worry about tomorrow, for tomorrow will worry about itself. Each day has enough trouble of its own." We should have a healthy concern for the future since we will live the rest of our lives there. It becomes problematic when we are so focused on the future that we forget to live for today.

When going through a rough period, you will spend a great deal of time trying to figure everything out. Remember that a situation that may seem impossible now may work itself out as the future unfolds.

God's advice is to concern ourselves with today, not tomorrow. You don't need to figure everything out today. The only thing you have to figure out <u>today</u> is what you can do <u>today</u>.

**Are you focused on <u>today</u>?**

**Are you more focused on the past? If so, what about the past is consuming so much of your attention?**

**Are you more future-minded? It is okay to think about and plan for the future but are you doing that at the expense of living in the present?**

## "Some Things Don't Make Sense" File

You set goals, plan, strive, and push to make your life all that you imagined it could be, and then life whacks you upside the head with the proverbial two-by-four. It was nowhere in my plans or dreams that one day my incredibly gifted daughter would be lost in the belly of her drug addiction Beast. My goals didn't include living with my Beast.

Jordan never planned for her life to be where she is today. Nobody says, "When I grow up, I'm going to be a drug addict." Not one parent thinks, "I can't wait for this precious little baby to shatter my heart." You will never hear a woman say, "I cannot wait to be married and abused by my husband."

*"Life is what happens to you while you're busy making other plans."*
— *"Beautiful Boy," John Lennon*

We all start out in life with hopes and dreams, and then life happens. If life has happened to you while you were busy making other plans, then you will need to make new plans and dream new dreams.

Have you ever thought "this really can't be happening," or "this can't be my life?" You are not alone. I know approximately one person whose life appears to be going exactly as planned. Hopefully, she has flexibility built into her life plan, as not even she will escape life without hardship, trials, or heartbreak.

At times, I still have those out of body experiences where I can't believe what has happened. The other day I was discussing something with a family member when I felt the waves of disbelief come crashing in one more time. I heard myself speaking, yet found it hard to believe the words were coming out of my mouth, even though I have been dealing with it for years.

We are all looking for a place to file things in our minds. We agonize over tragedies or a sudden loss, finding it hard to reconcile what has happened, to what we anticipated or expected.

When something happens that you aren't sure where to file in your mind, you need to make a new file. Let's call the new file, "Some Things Don't Make Sense." That is where I have begun to file the drug addiction Beast nightmare.

Filing your tragedy or pain somewhere in your mind will not necessarily lessen the ache in your heart, but it may provide some peace, allowing you to begin to accept what has happened.

 **What do you need to file in your "Some Things Don't Make Sense" file?**

## Stop Skipping School

Did you ever skip school? I did. I had no interest in science and yawned during geography. Just because I made an A or a B didn't mean I had retained what I learned. My philosophy was - information in long enough to make the grade, and then information out. Of course, I retained a great deal, but not enough. I should have taken school more seriously; I probably shouldn't have skipped so many classes.

As we go through life, we are always in school. You will find teachers everywhere: at work, on television or your computer, in social circles, at the grocery store, and even at home. Words of wisdom can be found in books, videos, movies, on the internet, and coming out of the mouth of a child. Too often, we skip the class and miss the lesson.

Some of the most valuable lessons you will ever learn will be through your trials. One of your life's best teachers may be your Beast.

While I was merely putting up with my Beast, I couldn't have cared less about learning much from my experience; I simply wanted it to stop. I desperately needed my daughter back, I wanted my family to be whole again, and I wanted relief from the agony.

As I began to battle, I understood there were lessons to learn, so I got ready. I put on my best dress, grabbed my books and headed to "school." My pencils were sharpened, my notebook empty, the pages of my lesson books crisp. I was eager to learn.

Before long, the class became demanding and painful. It didn't take long before my eagerness to learn the lesson diminished. It was all I could do to open the book, so I started to skip the class. Soon, I was skipping school altogether.

The most challenging lessons in life's school are those that involve emotions. I don't mind the challenge of solving a problem, but once the heart is involved, an ordinary lesson turns into a trigonometry class.

Some of our lessons in life have been incredibly painful. The lessons you learn while riding your Roller Coaster From Hell and from battling your Beast will be the most painful, yet the most valuable. Much of what I learned, I did so, kicking and screaming. You can skip class all you want and even flunk the grade, but you will be put right back where you started until you learn the lesson.

It may seem impossible in your current situation, for anything good to come of it. This may be especially true if there is no closure in sight. I know firsthand what it is to put your life on hold while your world is falling apart. My daughter is still an addict. Now and then, she gets "clean" for short periods of time. While I feel a sense of hope, I temper that hope with the reality that there is a likelihood of a relapse to follow.

You may be angry and feel as if life has dealt you a pretty unfair hand. I encourage you to take a deep breath and be open to the possibility of learning some valuable lessons. This type of personal growth cannot be learned by reading a book or hearing a story. Unfortunately, you will never learn from others' battles, what you can from your own.

 **Have you been skipping "school?"**

 **What is it that you need to learn but are resisting?**

## From Beast to Best

It's easy to be your best when everything is going right. It is when life smacks you upside the head with that two-by-four that you discover what you're made of. We rarely grow when things are going our way. Why would we? You have never been in a better position to become the best version of yourself than you are right now.

For a few years, we lived on Key Biscayne, a small island in the Biscayne Bay off the shore from Miami. We were never in a hurricane; however, we did experience quite a few strong tropical storms. After near hurricane force winds, surprisingly most of the palm trees were still standing. Palm trees are tremendously flexible. In fact, they can bend right down to the ground without breaking. What is even more interesting is that after the storm batters and bends the palm tree, it comes out of the storm stronger than it was before.

You are similar to the palm tree. The Beast can bring a storm into your life and even bend you to your breaking point, but with an attitude of flexibility and determination, you will come out stronger than you were before.

The Beast may have had you down on the mat, but ultimately the only one that can keep you down is you. Stand up and become better and stronger than you were before all hell broke loose. No matter where you are, no matter what your Beast looks like, you can move from Beast to Best.

## Still Standing

You will stumble, and you will fall. It doesn't matter how many times you fall. The only thing that matters is that you get up one more time than you fall down.

Your unique story has the potential to inspire and empower others. It's time for you to make the decision that no matter how many storms come upon you, like the palm tree, you will not break.

When the Beast tries to wrestle you back to the mat, laugh in his face. Be resolved that your Battle will end in victory. Be determined that when the dust settles, you will be standing over your Beast, stronger and better than you were before the battle.

## Start Growing Now

Don't wait for your circumstances to change before you begin to change. The small spark that ignites your fire of change will catch like wildfire. This spark is a very small first step that will set things in motion. Change yourself, and your circumstances will change.

Although you begin to change, certain aspects of your story may not change, at least not right away. Just because I began to be a better me, didn't cause Jordan to stand up and fight. In fact, coincidentally, when I stood up to fight, Jordan was far from battling her Beast. My fight didn't have a bearing on Jordan's but had I not stood up when I did, I would have been devastated by where her life is today.

I cringe at the thought of where I would be today had I not made the decision when I did. If I had waited for Jordan's life to change for the better in order for mine to change, I would be in a world of hurt.

I repeat - don't wait for your circumstances to change before you begin to change. Start now, right where you are.

 **What can you do to start growing right where you are?**

## Keep the End in Mind

I know a whole lot less about life than I thought I would at my age, but I know one thing for certain - nobody is getting out alive. It's creepy to think about death. I am sure you have been awake in the dark of night thinking about death; one day you are here and in an instant, you will be gone.

Consider the legacy you will leave behind after you are gone. Think about the impact your life will have on those who love you, the people who interacted with you on your journey through life. Even if you live to a ripe old age, realistically, there will be only two or three generations who would know you well enough to remember you when you are gone. By the third generation, most of us will be a distant memory; an old family photograph.

The point here is not to cause you to become depressed, but to make you think about the legacy you are creating. You may only have two or three generations of people who remember you once you are gone, but your impact on their lives can go on for many more generations.

My goddaughter was given my middle name. Her parents told me they wanted their daughter to grow up to be like me. Initially, I was humbled and honored by those words. Then it hit me. What if she grew up to become a woman smiling on the outside, and dying on the inside? I didn't want to think about that possibility.

When your time on earth is done, what will people remember? Let us take a few minutes to consider that question. Picture your memorial service. If you prefer, read this section, then close your eyes, sit in silence and go through the process. Before you begin, let me caution you to not be too hard on yourself. Nobody is watching you go through this exercise so try not to be so humble that you forget all of the positive things that will be said about you.

Take a deep breath and picture it. Where is the service taking place - a place of worship, a country club, a private home? Possibly near a lake, along a riverbank, or on top of a mountain. As the people in your life gather to remember you, are they silent, or are they sharing memories? Through their tears, do you hear laughter; can you see their smiles as they recall their time with you?

The service is about to begin. People are making their way to their seats. Music plays in the background; what kind of music is playing; is it a particular song? The music begins to fade. In the absence of music, you hear sniffling, soft crying, an occasional sob. As you look out over the crowd, who do you see? Look at the faces of the people who have come to pay tribute to your life.

Somebody stands up to deliver your eulogy. Is it a pastor, priest or rabbi? Is it a friend or family member; someone who knows you well? What do they say?

Once the eulogy is delivered, it's time for people representing different groups to stand up and speak. They are instructed to be completely honest and hold nothing back.

First, a family member stands and begins to speak on behalf of the family. Who is speaking and what are they saying about what you meant to the family?

Next, a friend stands up on behalf of all of your friends and explains what kind of a friend you were, and how much you will be missed. How did this person describe you?

A co-worker or business associate stands next to share a side of your life most of your family and friends did not see. Does this representative from your work life describe you as hard working, respectful, and honest? Did the business or organization lose a valued member of the team? What do they say?

One person gets up to explain your role in a club, church, or group. What was it about you they felt compelled to share with your friends and family?

Lastly, your spouse or partner stands up. This person is trembling; finding it hard to speak. When they finally do, is it because they are overwhelmed by their loss, or because they are required to tell the truth? How do they describe your private relationship and how your loss has impacted them?

As the service wraps up, from the back of the room, another person stands up and asks if they may speak for a moment. The crowd quiets and all eyes are upon this person who looks around nervously at the unfamiliar faces.

"Hello, I represent all of the store clerks, gas station attendants, restaurant servers, grocery store workers, and gardeners; all of the service providers the departed interacted with on this earth. As I'm required to speak truthfully, I must tell you that…"

How does this person describe you? Do they say you were courteous, respectful, and thankful to the people who served you in your community and beyond? Or, do they explain sadly, that you treated them rudely; that you appeared to take your unhappiness out on strangers?

It is one thing to be kind to the people we love. It is quite another for complete strangers or service people to say they will miss their interaction with you.

There were a lot of questions thrown at you and much to consider. This exercise may have been exhausting. If you feel good about how you would be remembered, then I applaud you. In your make believe memorial service, many people shared some wonderful things about you. However, it is possible a couple of things that were said made you squirm in your seat. There are aspects of our personalities we would all prefer nobody brought up. It is okay; nobody is perfect.

Here is the good news - you can change the outcome! You can't change the past, and there will always be situations you wish you could take back. If you take action now to become better, to allow yourself to grow and change your memorial service can turn out far better than you just imagined.

 **How did you feel as you went through the exercise?**

 **Did you smile as you pictured friends and family remembering you?**

**Would you prefer to be remembered differently? If so, you still have time to make changes.**

### Fitting the Pieces Together

When you **Stand <u>On</u> Your Story,** you will have more courage to **Decide to Stand Up and Fight** when you are knocked down. Owning your story will make it much easier to **Change Your Attitude** and to **Adjust Your Focus.** When you start to become a better version of yourself, you will automatically want to **Make Meaning From the Madness.** Standing strong will give you the perspective needed to **Put On Your Oxygen Mask, Get On Your Spiritual Armor** and **Build Your Circle of Strength.** As you stand <u>on</u> your story, you will give yourself the strength to **Stop Being a Control Freak.**

## Your Declaration

By completing the blanks of the Stand On Your Story Declaration, you are choosing to become a better person for having traveled your journey. You are committing to learning the lessons that your journey offers.

---

### Stand On Your Story Declaration

I, _____ am in a battle with a Beast. My Beast is: _____

_____

Today, _____, 20_____ I Stand <u>On</u> My Story, not in it. I shed the shame, guilt and stigma, and will no longer be anonymous. I declare that I will become more, not in spite of my story, but because of it.

_____
Signed

*www.ValerieSilveira.com*

---

## Faith in the Battle

*"You are the light of the world. A town built on a hill cannot be hidden. Neither do people light a lamp and put it under a bowl. Instead they put it on its stand, and it gives light to everyone in the house. In the same way, let your light shine before others, that they may see your good deeds and glorify your Father in heaven."*

**Matthew 5:14-16**

This verse came to mind when I thought about the action, Stand on Your Story. You see, I am not necessarily proud of how I handled myself during many years of this journey. My thoughts and actions certainly didn't even come close to being the "light of the world." There was no way I could let my light shine because the pit I was in was too dark and too deep to climb out of. I wanted a happy ending before I felt "worthy" to share this trial that seemed to have no purpose, no value. I had so many questions I still needed answered before I could stand on my story. Why had this trial come into my life to begin with? Why my son? Why our family? What could we have done differently? What would be the outcome of this story for our lives? Would my son, my marriage, our family even survive it? We want all our stories to be those of happy endings. But, as Valerie puts it, "there are no crystal balls," and we have no guaranteed outcomes either.

What this journey has taught me is that I was trying to write myself, my wants, and my intents into the pages of my son's story. But, there came a point in his life when he began to write his own story with the choices he made. Our stories, while still intertwined in places, had become separate and unique. It was at this point that I could only write my legacy in his heart and allow him to move forward and write his own autobiography. With hope in my heart, I wait with anticipation to read those pages believing they will be filled with laughter and sorrow, success, and a few momentary failures. I believe it will be the story of an overcomer, of a brave man who stood up to his Beast and beat it! Most of all, it is my utmost prayer that his story will speak of Jesus meeting him in that dark place of hopelessness and despair, where he had given up on his dreams long ago, and pulling him into his loving arms where he finds life and freedom again.

When I finally decided to stand on my own story, I felt exposed and vulnerable. In an attempt to protect my son and my family, I had hidden a part of my story that had permanently changed me as a person. I tried to protect myself by skirting around questions about our family, and I avoided any honest answers as to what we were really going through…which was basically hell on earth. How could I stand on my own story when it made absolutely no sense to me why I was living it in the first place? Standing on my story meant telling my whole story, the good, the bad, and the ugly despite what others might think. I believe if I had kept silent much longer, my Beast would have eaten me alive from the inside out. Seriously! I had to file all my "why" questions in my "Some Things Don't Make Sense File" and release my need for answers if I could begin to heal and move forward. I had to learn to trust and believe that my story has meaning and there is a purpose in sharing it. More importantly, I had to know that God loves me and cares about my story and that He has a purpose in writing it into the pages of my life. Your story has a purpose as well. It is one of a journey from despair to hope, and ultimately victory. It is time to let your light shine.

 **Look up the scriptures below and write them out.**

**2 Corinthians 3:3**

**Psalm 107:2**

**Psalm 71:15**

**Ask the Lord to reveal to you not why your story happened in the first place, but instead, what purpose He has in writing it. How can He be glorified in it? How can others be helped by telling it?**

**How have you grown while riding this roller coaster from hell? What have you learned through it? Take time now to start to write an outline of your story. Look for those hidden treasures of the heart in your story and write what He shows you.**

One very valuable lesson I learned by not skipping school was that my son and I are two totally separate people. Before that, I felt if I let go, I was giving up, and my Control Freak Beast did not like failure! In doing so, I stayed stuck. I was unable to grow into all God intended for me to be. This seems to be the case for most of us who struggle with being control freaks. We all too easily allow our roles and labels in life to define us. Good or bad, we accept and wear them without thought of who we really are on the inside. I have a confession to make. I got married at the age of eighteen, so that means I have been married a very long time. I got married before I had a clue who I was as a person on the inside. It was easy for me to fit into the role that my family had me in, but to have to switch roles and become an adult with adult responsibilities and a wife with wifely responsibilities, now that was a whole new ballgame. I often felt like I was juggling dozens of hats while I tried to figure out which one to wear for each occasion. I put on the best hat and identified with the role I was in, never giving thought to who I really was as a person. Perhaps you can identify with a loss of identity or maybe, like me, you never really had one in the first place.

In **1 Samuel 16:7b** we read, "The Lord does not look at the things people look at. People look at the outward appearance, but the Lord looks at the heart."

**Take a few minutes to reflect on your qualities as a person, not the roles or labels you fill. Write them here.**

**Read the following scriptures and note what they say about your beauty and value in God's eyes.**

1 Peter 3:3-4

Matthew 10:29-31

**Proverbs 31:28-30**

The most important lesson you can learn if you are going to stand on your story is that God believes in you. Your story is not over. You no longer need to be stuck waiting for others to change before you can stand on it. While you may not have any control over your loved ones, you do have influence. They are watching you. Your words and actions serve to remind them that you will always love them and never stop praying for them. You are writing quite a story and contrary to what you might believe, it is a story worth standing on.

**Read the following scriptures and note what your trials are accomplishing in your life.**

**James 1:2-4**

**Isaiah 40:31**

**Romans 5:3-5**

Valerie ran us through an exercise earlier that required me to be painfully honest with myself. She asked us to visualize our own memorial service upon our death in vivid detail. It was a challenge to me because as much as I am a people-person, I really do not like being the center of attention, especially at my own memorial service. But it did make me think long and hard about keeping my eyes on the finish line of my life and not being distracted by the detours along the way. My story is not over until God says it's over. What I will have left is my legacy. Not so long ago, I told my husband he had permission to write on my tombstone, "She worried herself to death." When I heard myself say that, I knew something had to change; and it has, day by day, because when my life is over, I want my tombstone to read in big, bold letters, "SHE TRUSTED GOD!"

Perhaps now is a good time to go back and review that exercise. Would you change anything? Would you rewrite your story? Spend some time in reflection and make any changes knowing that the God who made heaven and earth loves you very much, and He already has written a beautiful end to your story.

*"For every child of God defeats this world, and we achieve this victory through our faith."*
**1John 5:4 NLT**

*"Be sure you put your feet in the right place, then stand firm."*
~ **Abraham Lincoln**

"No matter where you are in your journey, you can make a
difference right now. People are watching you. When someone sees
you getting up off the mat after your Beast has knocked you down,
they begin to believe that they can stand up too."

**— Valerie Silveira**

## Action Introduction

It is no accident you are reading this book at this time. Before I attempt to convince you that you have what it takes to make a difference, let us take a moment to acknowledge that you feel like crap. Your heart is broken, and your soul is bruised. You are mentally, emotionally, physically, and spiritually exhausted, and I have the audacity to suggest you extend a hand to others.

You might be tempted to blow through this Action or skip it altogether. You may be convinced you're in no position to make meaning from the madness that has become your life. Did I somehow miss the reality that you have been through hell?

No, that reality has not escaped me. I have been there, and to a smaller degree, I'm still there. If I understand where you are, then how is it I could possibly believe you have the ability to make a difference in another person's life when you're barely holding it together yourself?

In a million years, I couldn't have imagined my child would become an addict, or that I would stand up and share my painful story. Perhaps you couldn't have imagined what has happened to you, but maybe there is something that can come out of your pain, something good, that you couldn't have imagined in a million years.

You are in a position to reach other people right where you are; the time is right for you to start making a difference because you are still battling. Yes, you heard it right. Not in spite of your circumstances, but because of where you stand right now.

People want and need to hear from real people who have been through something painful. You have credibility because of your battle. You are relatable because you are still in the battle. If you're bloodied and battle-worn, yet you're still in the fight, it will give other people courage to stand up and begin to fight their own battle.

When you take one tiny step forward to reach out to someone else in need, you will get back far more than you give. It is true that we get more by giving than we do by receiving. Amazing things will begin to happen when you find the courage to share your story or to reach out to someone else.

First, you will be energized and empowered by helping others. When you share your story, your battle, at first you may not be sure what to say. Eventually, you will find wisdom pouring out of you that you were not conscious of until the words flowed from your lips. There is a fountain of knowledge, experience, and wisdom trapped inside of you just waiting to be unleashed.

There are times in which the teacher becomes the student. I have found myself in situations where I have been offering guidance or wisdom to someone only to have the other person say something so profound that I couldn't wait to write it down. They weren't typically aware that what they said was going to be so meaningful to me. It can often be something very simple, yet brilliant. No doubt, they left the conversation wondering where in the world their own wisdom came from.

It makes no difference how old you are, or what obstacles you have faced. It is never too late, or too soon to begin to Make Meaning From the Madness.

## People Are Watching You

We were selling our house in 2006. One of my brothers was helping me to paint the deck railing. It was a warm summer day, and we were each lost in our thoughts until he broke the silence.

"We were talking about you and Rich the other day."

"Yeah, what about?" I tried to act nonchalant.

While Jordan was crashing, our finances had taken a hit as well. It had been a rough few years to that point. He went on to explain that he and another brother had been discussing the strain all of this must be having on our marriage.

"We've been watching you, and we're amazed at how well you're handling everything. We can't believe you're still married. You even seem to still like each other!"

I chuckled, and then we returned to our painting. It had never occurred to me that other people were watching. I was just trying to survive. Not only were other people watching, but they were inspired. People were watching me; they were watching Rich, and they were watching us.

People are watching you, whether you realize it or not. Stand in the confident knowledge that you can come out of this stronger, wiser, and with more courage. Your resolve to stand and Battle Your Beast is not just about winning the battle; it's also about the opportunity that you have to inspire others.

Most people are intrigued by athletes, actors, or royalty. They are impressed by the people who have changed the world of sports, technology or medicine. The masses can't seem to get enough of folks who have special talents or abilities. People are in awe of celebrities who are simply famous for being famous.

The people who inspire us most, those that captivate our hearts, are the people who have been to hell and back. The world cheers for the heroes, who have, against all odds, risen off the mat. It is the person who has battled their Beast whom we admire most. People are watching you, and they are waiting to be inspired and empowered by you.

 **Are you aware that people might be watching you?**

 **Can you think of ways in which you could positively affect others just by the mere fact that they are around you?**

 **Who might be impacted by you, not directly, but by watching as you begin to make meaning from the madness?**

## You Don't Have to Be Mother Teresa

You may be overwhelmed at the thought of making a difference. When you think of difference makers, what types of people come to mind? Perhaps you think of social workers, visionaries, tech gurus, motivational speakers, pastors, or missionaries. Bill Gates changed the way the world communicates. Martin Luther King gave his life, spreading a message of love and equality. There are countless individuals who have made a massive difference in the lives of thousands or millions of people.

Mother Teresa made a vow of chastity, poverty, obedience, and to serve to the poorest of the poor. If you compare yourself to one of these people, you may want to pull the covers over your head and go back to sleep.

You don't have to be Mother Teresa to make a difference. Search your heart. Think of all you have been through and how much knowledge, wisdom and personal growth you have gained. Consider your gifts and talents. Don't wait until you come up with an earth-shattering venture to begin Making Meaning. Little things are big things.

The last thing Jordan remembers from the night she was shot was being strapped to a backboard and wheeled into an aid car. She was vomiting and going into shock.

She asked the emergency medical responder, "Am I going to die?"

He told her, "Not in my truck."

This man could have easily judged Jordan for being involved in this type of incident. He could have looked down on her for even being in that area of the city. He could have easily ignored Jordan's question, after all, he was busy trying to save her life. Instead of ignoring her question, he provided a moment of peace to a terrified girl, in what could have been her last memory.

Somehow, I hope this man finds his way to my book. I pray that he realizes he is the one who drove into a neighborhood where bullets had been flying only minutes before. He will remember placing Jordan on a backboard and transporting her to Harborview Medical Center. I want him to know that at least one mother has never forgotten what he did for her daughter. I want him to know that the little thing he said that night was a big thing.

 **What little thing can you do now, that could end up being a big thing?**

## Begin Now

Rather than wait until you have everything figured out, which will be, never, step out and begin to Make Meaning From the Madness.

When you begin to make meaning in your life, you may find you receive much more in return than you have given. You may not see it at first, but it will happen the more time you spend in the service of others.

Go ahead and give it a try. There is one caveat, though. Whatever you do, you must do it with <u>no expectation of receiving anything in return.</u> It is absolutely necessary to give with no expectation. Don't be surprised when you are repaid for your generosity and courage. Not only are others watching, but God is watching.

Don't get caught up in scorekeeping. If you never make the connection between something you did and what comes your way later, it is okay. You never know when a kind gesture now will be repaid to you down the road.

The worst-case scenario is that your selflessness will make you feel good. Your newfound courage, wisdom, and empowerment will cause you to stand a little stronger than you did the day before. You will begin to build the belief that your story matters.

 **As much as you might resist this notion, consider three reasons why you might be just the person to overcome this situation and to inspire and empower others:**

**1.**

**2.**

**3.**

## Well Done

Some of us have taken the harder road through life. Mine has been exciting, weary, confident, uncertain, courageous, terrifying, unpredictable, disciplined, meaningful, meaningless, fun, heartbreaking, hopeful, comfortable, uncomfortable, painful, manageable, and out of control.

*"Life should not be a journey to the grave with the intention of arriving*
*safely in a pretty and well-preserved body, but rather to skid in*
*broadside in a cloud of smoke, thoroughly used up, totally worn out, and*
*loudly proclaiming*
*"Wow! What a Ride!"*
*— Hunter S. Thompson*

One day I will skid broadside in a cloud of smoke, totally worn out, and my ride will be over. Someday your ride will be over too. When mine is over, and I stand at the gates of heaven, first I hope my name will be on the list! Assuming the gate angel finds my name, I will be called to stand before my maker for a little trip down my life's memory lane.

I'm sort of hoping God and I don't really have to watch the movie together; after all, we have both seen it. Is it really necessary to go over every gory detail again?

If we do, there will be scenes in my life story that will cause me to cover my eyes, to plug my ears. I may have to watch much of it peeking through my fingers. As the scenes of my life unfold, God will smile, and a time or two he will no doubt chuckle. He may downright laugh out loud.

During certain scenes, God might close his eyes or shake his head. While watching others, tears will stream down both of our cheeks. As the last scene flashes by and the credits roll, I will look sheepishly at God, holding my breath in anticipation of what he might say.

My hope and prayer is that when all things are taken into consideration, he will whisper,

"Well done."

When the credits roll on your life's movie, it won't necessarily matter how it began or what happened near the middle. It isn't important whether your story was a serious drama, comedy or a real tearjerker. What matters is there is still time to change. If you're breathing, you still have time to add more scenes to your life's movie; to Make Meaning from the Madness.

Maybe you don't even believe in God. Still, at the end of our lives, we all want to know that someone, somewhere, will think or say, "Well Done."

 **Write yourself a letter or a note, acknowledging all of the things in your life to this point and those that you are working on, for which you deserve to hear, "Well Done."**

If you have gone through this entire Workbook, I commend you - Well Done! You are on your way to the day when you will be standing in victory over your Beast.

### Fitting the Pieces Together

Understanding you can **Make Meaning From the Madness** gives you hope, and therefore you will be more likely to **Decide to Stand Up and Fight**. Knowing your life is bigger than you will help you to **Get On Your Spiritual Armor** and **Build Your Circle of Strength**. Realizing the opportunity to make meaning, you will want to **Change Your Attitude** and **Adjust Your Focus,** which will give you the courage to **Put On Your Oxygen**

**Mask** and **Stand <u>On</u> Your Story**. The realization that you're not the only person to have ridden the Roller Coaster from Hell will provide perspective to help you to **Stop Being a Control Freak.**

## Your Declaration

Complete the Make Meaning From the Madness declaration. You are committing that you will not wait until everything settles out in your life in order to start making a difference. You will begin to make meaning from the madness today!

---

### Make Meaning From the Madness Declaration

I, _____ am in a battle with a Beast. My Beast is: _____

_____

Today, _____, 20_____ I declare that I am making my life matter. I have much to offer, right where I am, and I understand that I don't have to be Mother Teresa to make a difference. I will start now, Making Meaning From the Madness.

_____

Signed

---

## Faith in the Battle

While recently contemplating the toll our journey has had on our family, it came to me that probably no one was more affected than my daughter, our youngest child, who has been diagnosed with Asperger's, a form of high functioning autism. Living with an Autism Spectrum disorder has meant that, every day, she fights to fit into a world that is uncomfortable for her. Circumstances can easily overwhelm her if they become too chaotic, causing her to want to make a beeline for the comfort of her own room. It hit me how hard it must have been for her to grow up with an addiction Beast living under the same roof as her. Not only did she experience firsthand the madness of having her older brother taken hostage by a life controlling addiction, but she also witnessed her mom being smothered by her own Beasts of codependency and enabling. She was cueing off my actions and reactions, and it was taking a toll on her as well. If I was going to make meaning out of this complete and total madness we were living in, I had to realize that like it or not, people (and my daughter) were watching me.

It took years for me to begin to share my story with family and friends who did not have a child suffering from addiction. Along with that admission came my first instinct, to apologize for not being "present" for them the last several years. I had pulled away from so many people partly because the whole experience of living with a loved one with an addiction is exhausting, emotionally and physically; but mostly to avoid feeling the need to justify my shortcomings as a mom and, perhaps, even as a Christian. It wasn't that I believed I was a horrible mom or that a lack of faith had brought this on, although those thoughts did cross my mind, but somewhere along the way, faith took a back seat to fear. I guess deep down I had to believe everything was going to work out okay, and I just could not let myself go "there" if it did not. Telling my story made it seem so much more REAL, more definite, and with that came the reality that we might not get our happy ending. I was finally willing to tell our story, my story, with all eyes on me. I felt like the leading character in the tale, The Emperor's New Clothes, parading around totally naked, with everyone else pretending I looked just fine. They were watching, and with God's help, I wanted to be more than fine. As the curtains rose and the stage lights brightened, it was time to make meaning out of this madness.

**Write out the following scriptures. As you do so, reflect on the people who are watching you and what impact you may be having on them.**

**2 Chronicles 16:9a**

**Psalm 34:11**

**Hebrews 10:24**

I have a big problem with perfectionism. Growing up, my faults were always pointed out to me, and it was usually in front of others. I found that in order to avoid embarrassment I would quit something I was not perfect at. That may sound unreasonable, but it was my defense mechanism growing up, and it worked for me, at least as a kid. As an adult, that simply did not work for me anymore. We all do the best we can in the roles we are called to, but quitting is not an option. As parents, our kids are watching us. As wives or sisters, our families are watching us. Our friends, neighbors, and colleagues are watching us. Pass or fail, we do not get a do-over, but we can make a difference perhaps in one person's life if we allow ourselves to be seen as we really are. As we try to make meaning from the madness, Valerie reminded us that we don't have to be Mother Teresa to make a difference. I doubt I will ever be canonized, but I do hope I will be remembered for making a difference for the better in just one person's life.

There is a section in the workbook that is short and sweet called, "Begin Now." I love this section because Valerie basically says, "Just do it!" She challenged us to get outside our own lives and heads and be of service to others. It was at that point in the book that I felt led to work with Valerie on this Christian version of the workbook. What an amazing challenge it has been and what an awesome blessing. Has my son gotten off his own roller coaster from hell? Gratefully, at this moment he is working on his recovery and making slow and steady progress. I continue to pray for him and for his recovery as well as his relationship with the Lord. But even if he wasn't, because of the grace of God, I can say I am making lemonade out of these really sour lemons I've been given.

In the standard version of Valerie's Workbook, she explains her Meaning from the Madness Lemonade. She had us go in and make our own lemonade recipe using the tools we learned from the Nine Actions and the gifts and talents we bring. For this version of the Workbook, we removed that exercise in favor of something a little sweeter, fruit punch instead of lemonade. Let's look at the recipe.

 **When the Holy Spirit is present in our hearts, He produces some succulently sweet fruit in our lives. Read the following scripture and circle the ingredients necessary to make Fruit of the Spirit Fruit Punch.**

*"But the Holy Spirit produces this kind of fruit in our lives: love, joy, peace, patience, kindness, goodness, faithfulness, gentleness, and self-control."* **Galatians 5:22-23**

Have you ever started working on a recipe, only to discover that you are missing one of the ingredients? To make the perfect punch, we need the perfect balance of sour and sweet. Spiritually speaking, the Spirit adds the "sweetest" fruit to our punch (our lives) in just the right amount at just the right time. Suddenly the bitterness of our sour circumstances tastes a little bit sweeter.

**Which of these ingredients is missing from your recipe right now?**

There are times when our circumstances have caused us to become bitter. We feel forgotten, misunderstood, and resentful. **1 Thessalonians 5:16-19** tells us to "Rejoice always, pray continually, give thanks in all circumstances; for this is God's will for you in Christ Jesus. Do not quench the Spirit." Perhaps our recipe is missing a little sweetness because we believe we do not have much to rejoice about or be thankful for. Now's the time to let the Lord sweeten things up and makes us better, not bitter.

**How might having the fruit of the Spirit at work in you help you better deal with your own Beasts of codependency and enabling or any other Beast you might be struggling with?**

**In what ways does having the fruit of the Spirit better equip you to make wise decisions concerning your loved one or the battle with your own Beast?**

Our fruit punch, while it may be tasty, will only make us fat if we don't drink it with the intent of giving back to others and Making Meaning from the Madness. The Addiction Beast is by far one of the most selfish Beasts I personally have ever run across. Our codependency and enabling Beasts, while they may seem to be "other-centered," are also selfish because they want to keep us all to themselves. They, like many other Beasts, want us to hibernate in that old, dark cave and drown in our own circumstances and sorrows. If we are not trying to fix other people or control every situation, they convince us our lives are void of any real meaning or purpose. But God says otherwise! One of the most inspiring verses in the bible to me is **Proverbs 31:25-26**, "She is clothed with strength and dignity; she can laugh at the days to come. She speaks with wisdom, and faithful instruction is on her tongue." The entire chapter is worth reading and re-reading as it reminds us of the power and influence we have as women, especially as Christian women.

As we grasp the reality that there is a hurting and lost world out there whose only hope is in their own abilities, we can begin to see our power of influence to bring true hope and light into their lives. Our circumstances did not happen by mistake. They did not catch God off guard. He has the power to stop that person you care so much about from hurting themselves or others, but He will not interrupt their God-given right to choose their own path, and that is why He gave them (and us) free will in the first place. He also has the power to rid our lives of our own Beasts instantly if He so chooses, but while that might be easier for us, true transformation comes from putting in the hard work. He longs for hearts that want to serve Him, not those that have to serve Him. Making Meaning from our Madness embraces the wisdom that comes from knowing and trusting in His plan and acting on it. Like Valerie, I think of this crazy life I have lived, what a ride it has been, and what is yet waiting around the next turn to be experienced to its fullest. As I contemplate it, I can feel apprehension, or I can let go and feel the anticipation. The choice is mine, and it is yours as well. Today, I am grateful that my trials are turning into triumphs. Who would have ever thought I could say that? I am grateful and honored to be able to give others the hope He has given me. It is my prayer that you will also Make Meaning from Your Madness, and on that final day together we will all hear those precious words, "Well Done."

*"His master replied, "Well done, good and faithful servant! You have been faithful with a few things; I will put you in charge of many things. Come and share your master's happiness."*

**Matthew 25:21**

## *Valerie- On Keeping the Pieces Together*

I put the pieces of my broken heart back together while my daughter was still lost in the belly of her Beast. I fought my Beast after my heart had been broken into a million pieces. I stood up and took my life back while a dark cloud hung over my scarred heart. You may be in a similar situation.

Putting the pieces back together after your situation becomes smoother would be less challenging, but you can't afford to wait.

Once you are standing over your Beast, it will feel great. However, it is critical that you stay vigilant. The Beast won't stay down. Truthfully, the most challenging part of the putting the pieces back together may be, keeping them together. Since my daughter is a drug addict, she will have a lifelong battle with her Beast (if she ever decides to stand up and fight). Therefore, I too have a lifelong battle to keep standing; to keep the pieces of my heart together.

You will need to use the Nine Actions to Battle Your Beast on a continual basis. These Actions are meant to be used for the rest of your life, in order for you to remain standing, and to grow stronger and more courageous with each passing day. Let them become a part of your everyday life.

If I can do this, you can too. You have what it takes to battle your Beast, whatever that Beast may be. You possess more courage, strength, and wisdom than you give yourself credit for having. When you look to your right, or to your left, I hope you can picture me standing shoulder to shoulder with you.

### Update to Valerie's Story

On the morning of August 29, 2016, I got that knock on the door; the knock all moms of addicts fear. As the mom of an addict, I was fully aware of the real possibility that my daughter would die from a drug overdose. It had not occurred to me that once again she would be shot. The night before that knock on the door, my daughter was murdered.

I had done the work in this book, so my Beast was very much under control. He would occasionally knock on my door, but I had learned not to answer it. That morning, he didn't bother to knock; he broke my door down – a home invasion.

This news dropped me to my knees. I rolled over onto my back, and my Beast got on top of me, in that comfortable place where he had been for so many years. For a short while, I didn't even want to get back up. My heart felt as if it was ripped right out of my chest. But I did get back up fairly quickly because I understood the very Actions I had been living would allow me to live with a hole in my heart.

I miss Jamie* every single day, but I also carry her memory with me. Her spirit is by my side, encouraging me; reminding me,

"I am so proud of you, mommy."

No matter what you have been through, or what your life looks like now, you too can find the courage and strength to stand. I hope it helps even a little bit, to know, that I am standing with you.


**\*Before her death, I referred to Jamie as "Jordan."**

# <u>*Dawn – On Keeping the Pieces Together*</u>

A dear friend and I always joke about life and have termed the phrase "keep it together" to be used when things are out of control, and all we seem to be doing is putting out fires. When she starts in about her life and the craziness going on, I will look at her and say, "keep it together," and likewise, she will do the same for me. We usually end up laughing as we try and figure out just how many more balls we can throw into the air and try to juggle. It may be funny to joke about it, but it is certainly not easy.

Keeping the pieces of my new normal life together is not easy either. The fragments are torn and frayed; they no longer fit together neatly with perfectly seamed edges. The tapestry of my life is interwoven with joy and laughter, happiness and hope. Carefully stitched into the secret places of my heart are moments of sadness and fears, uncertainty and doubt. They speak of the faithfulness of the Master Tailor, who chose to weave them into my life for his transforming purpose, all while I followed closely behind him with a seam ripper trying to tear them out, convinced he had made some sort of a mistake. Beautifully handcrafted by God, my tattered quilt of a heart is my offering back to him. Its frayed edges may not fit together seamlessly, but they are unique to me, to my story. Innate to my personality, any unexpected change is met with determined resistance on my part. I am still working on that, but I believe even my tenacity has been woven into my life for a purpose. I am humbled by this journey as it has brought me to a place of surrender and transformation.

The symbol of the Nine Actions is a beautiful purple heart that looks like a puzzle. Each piece represents one of the Nine Actions, and they all come together to form a pretty little heart. My heart was shattered when my son's Beast came into my life. It was crushed when my Beast joined in. The Lord used the Nine Actions and His superglue mix of faith, hope, and love to put it back together. The scar tissue that resulted only serves to make it stronger. Like yours, my story is far from over. I am grateful beyond words for Valerie and the Nine Actions. I am on this journey with you as together we stand against our Beasts and have the victory over them!

*"Search me, God, and know my heart; test me and know my anxious thoughts. See if there is any offensive way in me, and lead me in the way everlasting."* **Psalm 139:23-24**

# _Resources_

**Valerie's Resources:**

www.ValerieSilveira.com


Valerie's Books can be found on Amazon

www.Amazon.com/author/ValerieSilveira


**Dawn's Resources:**

www.DawnRWard.com

# About the Authors

**Valerie Silveira** is an award-winning Author, international Speaker, and Beast Slayer. She is helping thousands of people to stand up and fight; to reclaim their lives. She speaks out against the shame, guilt, and stigma that surrounds and suffocates so many people living with all types of Beasts.

As the mom of a daughter who lived half of her life with an addiction Beast, she knows the pain and paralyzing fear that other parents of addicts face. After losing her daughter to murder in August 2016, Valerie understands what it is to live with a hole in her heart. She is determined to spread her message of hope, and to share the Nine Actions to Battle Your Beast; actions that are changing lives, with as many people as possible. It has now become a labor of love that she shares with the spirit of her daughter, Jamie Lynn (a.k.a. Jordan).

**Dawn R. Ward** has served in Women's Ministry and Leadership for over thirty years. Professionally she works in the medical field, primarily with female patients, which gives her a unique perspective into the hearts and lives of women. Dawn has been married to the same wonderfully patient man for thirty-seven plus years and is the mother of three adult children, two who have struggled with addiction, and one who is on the Autism Spectrum. She understands how difficult it is to stand strong in the midst of trying to support hurting children. Her passion is to teach and equip women to live victorious lives of faith in spite of the hardships they find themselves facing.

# References

[i] http://content.time.com/time/health/article/0,8599,1912687,00.html

[ii] http://www.webmd.com/depression/guide/exercise-depression

[iii] Source: http://www.mayoclinic.org/stress-relief/art-20044456

[iv] Dictionary.com

Made in the USA
San Bernardino, CA
18 August 2018